GEORGE CARVER

Boy Scientist

GEORGE CARVER

CARVER

Boy Scientist

BY

Augusta Stevenson

ILLUSTRATED BY

Clotilde Embree Funk

THE BOBBS-MERRILL COMPANY

Publishers

INDIANAPOLIS   NEW YORK

DEDICATED TO
RACKHAM HOLT
MASTER BIOGRAPHER
OF GEORGE WASHINGTON CARVER

ACKNOWLEDGMENTS

The author wishes to acknowledge her indebtedness to Rackham Holt, author of *George Washington Carver, An American Biography*, from which excellent work valuable material was obtained, and to the following people who read the manuscript and offered suggestions: Elsie W. Stokes, Stokes & Stockell Bookstore, Nashville, Tennessee; Evelyn Sickels, Indianapolis Public Library; William L. Patterson, Director, Abraham Lincoln School, Chicago; and Cleo W. Blackburn, Director, Flanner House, Indianapolis.

CONTENTS

CHAPTER   PAGE

I   Night Riders   13

II   Insects, Weeds and a Lizard   28

III   The Plant Doctor   41

IV   Strawberries, School, Speller   55

V   How George Saved His Friend   69

VI   Strange Things Had Happened   81

VII   George's First School   91

VIII   George Goes to Kansas   103

IX   The Little Wanderer   112

X   Tucks, Pleats and Ruffles   121

XI   Artist George Carver   132

XII   Could It Be Rosie?   142

XIII   Discoveries   157

XIV   The Graduating Class   164

XV   Professor George Carver   185

LIST OF FULL-PAGE ILLUSTRATIONS

PAGE

Men on horses surrounded her.   24

No one saw the thin little Negro boy who sat
shivering on the log doorstep.   61

The back door opened and out came a nice-looking
Negro woman.   88

"Why!" the teacher exclaimed. "I thought
you had never gone to school."   92

A good-natured farmer stopped his team and
asked George to ride in his wagon.   114

He looked at the men closely—too closely.
One of them noticed it.   147

He dipped his fingers in the scum. Then he
smelled them. It was oil!   167

Now his name was called. He stood up.   182

The shabby colored man came through the gates.   197

I

NIGHT RIDERS

1. Moses Carver Fears a Raid

ONE morning around nine o'clock Mr. Moses Carver hurried to his log cabin and went in.

His wife was weaving. Mary, a young Negro slave, was spinning flax. They were both surprised to see Mr. Carver. They knew something had happened to bring him home now.

He always left the cabin at daylight and he never came back till dinnertime, at noon. He was a farmer here in southwestern Missouri and a hard-working one.

He wasted no time now. "I've news for you," he said grimly, "and it's bad news. Colonel Grant just told me. All of his slaves were stolen last night."

Mrs. Carver jumped to her feet and looked at her husband with frightened eyes. "Mose!" she cried. "Night Riders!"

"I've news for you," he said grimly, "and it's bad news."

"Yes, Sue, Night Riders."

Mary didn't speak but there was fright in her eyes, too. She tried to spin but her hands trembled.

She knew what happened when slaves were stolen by these riders. They were sold down south to work in swamps full of fever and snakes.

No wonder her hands trembled. No wonder
there was fright in her dark eyes—it might happen to her.

Mr. Carver was speaking again. "They're
nothing but a band of thieves. I thought the army
would get them when border warfare broke out
in 1860. But here it is 1861, and there's more of
them than ever."

"I didn't think they'd come here to Diamond
Grove," said Mrs. Carver. "There are no big
plantations and no one has many slaves. Colonel
Grant had only six. We have only Mary and her
two little children."

"No farm is too small for them now. Here
lately they're stealing horses, cattle and grain."

"Oh! I didn't know that."

"I didn't tell you; I knew you'd be frightened.
Now you must know; they may raid our farm
next."

"Tonight?"

"No, not that soon. They take the slaves down into Arkansas to sell, and that's a long trip. I don't expect them for a week or so."

"Marse Mose, did they take the children last night?"

"Yes, Mary, they did; every one of them."

"The babies, too?"

"The babies, too."

Mary broke down and sobbed. "My baby can't take that ride—he's too sick—he'd die from it."

"Don't cry, Mary," said Sue Carver gently. "We won't let them get your children. We'll all go up into the Ozark Mountains and hide. A good many people have gone there to get away from these raiders."

"We can't do that," said Moses. "I can't leave my horses and cattle."

"Take them along; that's what others did."

"I have too many; I couldn't get feed for them all up there."

"Then what will we do, Mose?"

"Colonel Grant has a plan. He wants the men in this neighborhood to watch the roads every night. We'll take turns and send word around when they come."

"That's a good plan," agreed Mrs. Carver. "It will give you a chance to hide in the woods, Mary—you and the children."

"Wish my husband was here to help me."

"Yes, I wish it, too," said Sue gravely.

"Maybe it's better he died, Miss Sue. Now I know the raiders can't sell him down south."

"You face the same thing, Mary, if they get you."

"They're not likely to get her," declared Moses. "I'll warn her in time and I'll help with the children. We'll hide in that cave back of the milkhouse."

"They'll never find you there," said Sue. "No

one knows about it except our neighbors. A stranger couldn't find it even in daytime."

"Yes, ma'am, I know it's safe if I can get there. I don't know; they come awful sudden."

"You must run the minute I warn you," said Moses. "I'll take Jim and you take the baby."

"And run for your life, Mary," said Sue. "Don't stop for anything, no matter what happens."

2. *Turk and His Thieves*

It was a week later and the first night of the half moon. Its light was dimmed by dark clouds but it was bright enough for a band of riders on the Diamond Grove road.

There were ten of them, all slave-stealers. Each carried a revolver in his belt. Their leader, a rascal called Turk, carried a rifle also.

Now the moon came from behind the dark clouds and shone brightly upon the riders.

"Drat this moonlight!" growled one.

"Who cares!" exclaimed another. "These Missouri people are all afraid of us."

'Does anyone know where we're going?" asked a third man.

"I don't know and I don't care," a mean-looking man answered. "Turk always knows where there's slaves. He's got a scout out looking around, a fellow named Grimes."

They rode in silence after that. Only the thud of galloping horses was heard as they flew along the dirt road.

A hunter put out his campfire the instant he heard this sound. A traveler on the road left it quickly and hid in the woods till the band passed by. A few persons peeped out from dark rooms. Others locked their doors and waited in fear of what might happen.

The band had now come to Goose Creek, a mile or so from the Carver farm. Turk stopped his horse and the others gathered about him.

"Grimes was to meet us here," he said. "We'll wait."

An hour passed. The men were getting impatient. The leader himself was worried. They listened for the sound of a running horse. And all the time the moon was rising higher and becoming brighter.

"It's a good night for a sheriff's posse," growled one of the thieves. "They like moonlight."

"Maybe they've caught Grimes," suggested another.

"They'll never get him; he's too smart," declared Turk. But he was only talking—he was afraid they had.

Then suddenly Grimes rode out of the woods and into the bunch of scowling men.

"We've been waiting for you a good hour," Turk said angrily.

"I'm lucky to get here at all," Grimes answered sharply.

"What's wrong? Some sheriff get after you?"

"No. Soldiers."

"Soldiers!" exclaimed Turk. "Didn't know there were any in this county."

"They've come lately. There's a big army camp about five miles from here, near Neosho. And the General said he was going to get every Night Rider in Missouri and put 'em in the army. It was in the Neosho newspaper."

"That's just talk," declared Turk. "They won't have time to hunt us. They've got to fight."

"They had time to get after me. I had to come through the woods to throw 'em off."

The thieves looked at Turk. He looked at Grimes for a moment. Then he turned to the others.

"We've got to get away from here," he said,

"and get away quick. We'll take the road to Arkansas."

"There's a farm we could raid on the way," Grimes suggested. "It wouldn't take ten minutes. There's only one slave."

"No! I'm not taking the risk just for one."

"She's only nineteen and she's strong and smart. She can do any kind of housework and she can cook and sew and weave."

"That means she's worth some money," said Turk.

"She is," said Grimes.

"Lead the way, Grimes! Ride fast, all of you!"

3. The Kidnaping

The half moon shone brightly into Mary's little cabin, so she knew it was getting late. It was ten o'clock at least and she should be in bed.

Instead, she put another stick of wood on the fire, for the night air from the hills was cold.

She might have to sit up all night with the baby. He had the whooping cough and she must give him honey.

He was quiet now and three-year-old Jim was sound asleep in the trundlebed. Mary took up her knitting.

Suddenly the cabin door was thrown open and Moses Carver rushed in.

"Riders!" he cried. "Run! Run!"

He snatched Jim from the bed and ran out with him. As Mary lifted baby George the blanket fell to the floor. Then she made the mistake of her life. She stopped to pick up the blanket and wrap it about the baby.

It took only a minute but when she turned to go she knew she was too late. She heard horses gallop up to her door. She heard men talking.

In another minute the cabin was full of men. The baby was taken out of her arms and she was dragged outside to a horse.

Men on horses

surrounded her.

Men on horses surrounded her. They thrust the reins into her hand and whipped her horse. In an instant they were all off—Mary in their midst and forced to gallop with them.

Mr. Carver sent a man to Arkansas after them the next day; a man who had been a Night Rider himself—Joe Bentley.

He was to steal Mary and the baby from the thieves and bring them back to Diamond Grove.

This was dangerous business, but Moses said he'd pay him well. He'd give him forty acres of good land and Pacer, a horse worth three hundred dollars.

In a week Bentley returned but Mary wasn't with him. He couldn't find her. No one had seen her. No one knew where the slave-stealers had gone.

But he had found baby George. The riders had

given him to some woman; they couldn't bother with a sick baby.

He had him now—that bundle tied to the back of his saddle.

"The woman gave him up," he said. "She didn't want to bother either—she thought he wouldn't live. But he's still alive. I took good care of him—the best I could.

"And I won't take your forty acres, Moses, because I didn't find Mary. I'll just take Pacer for my pay."

"You've earned him," said Moses.

"Of course that makes the baby cost you three hundred dollars but I reckon he's worth it to you: you thought so much of Mary."

"We did," said Sue. "It's like losing a member of our family."

"We'll find her sometime," declared Moses. "I won't give up looking for her."

II

INSECTS, WEEDS AND A LIZARD

1. In George's Pockets

A CUTE-LOOKING little Negro boy sneaked up to the cabin and peeped through the open door. He saw Mrs. Carver asleep in her chair and grinned with delight.

He crept into the room as softly as a cat. Then he tiptoed across it to the ladder that led to the loft.

He reached it. He had a foot on the first round when Mrs. Carver woke up.

"George!" she exclaimed. "What are you up to now?"

"I was just going up to the loft, Miss Sue."

"What for?"

"Oh—oh—I—I—was just going——"

"What's in your pockets, George?"

28

"Oh—nothing much——"

"You're bringing things into the house again!
What did I tell you about that?"

"They won't be in your way up there. I've got
some boxes to put them in."

"What is it this time? Snakes?"

"I found a pretty one. It won't hurt you."

"I won't have it in the house. I won't have the
rest of them either. Here, empty your pockets
into this basket."

George obeyed. Out came two frogs, six
beetles, four caterpillars, one granddaddy-long-
legs, one walking-stick, two big tobacco worms,
and one little garden snake.

"Now take them outside and turn them loose."

"All of them?"

"Every last one."

"I wanted to watch them."

"Then take them to the barn."

"The rats will get them out there."

"Then turn them loose. You cannot keep them in your bedroom and you're old enough to know why."

"I'm just going on seven."

Mrs. Carver smiled. "You needn't try to coax me, George. Take them out."

"Yes, ma'am."

Mrs. Carver watched him from the window. She noticed how gently he freed them.

"He loves them," she thought. "Poor little orphan—no father—no mother—no one but his brother. And Jim is only nine. I suppose I could let him keep some of the insects. They wouldn't be like frogs and snakes under your feet."

2. Knock! Knock! Knock!

"George," said Mrs. Carver that evening, "I don't care if you keep a few insects in your room."

Before George could speak a strange thing

happened. There were two loud knocks on the under side of the wooden seat of Mrs. Carver's chair. She jumped up quickly and screamed.

"What is it? What's the matter with you, Sue?" asked Mr. Carver. He was a little deaf and hadn't heard the strange noise.

"Something knocked on my chair—right under me! There were two knocks close together."

"I heard them," said Jim. "It scared me, too."

Just then there came two more knocks on the seat of the chair. This time Moses heard them.

"It's spirits!" whispered Sue. "They want to tell us something."

"I don't believe in spirits," said Moses. "I didn't know you did, Sue."

"I didn't but now I don't know. Maybe they know where Mary is. Maybe they're trying to tell us."

Knock! Knock! Again came the sound from the chair.

"You hear that?" Sue whispered. "It means, 'Yes, yes.' They do know about Mary."

"Maybe it's a warning," suggested Jim. "Maybe the Night Riders are coming again."

"It couldn't be that," declared Mrs. Carver. "They haven't been in Missouri for a long time. The soldiers got rid of them."

"Only for a time," said Mr. Carver. "I've been hearing about them just lately. They're riding again. I don't want you boys to play in your mother's cabin any more. It isn't safe."

Knock! Knock!

Everyone looked at the chair.

"Something terrible will happen," whispered Sue.

"It's mighty strange," admitted Moses.

Knock! Knock! Knock!

No one spoke. Then suddenly George went to the chair and put his hand under the seat.

"I've got it!" he cried. He held up his hand and in it was a good-sized lizard.

"Spirits!" laughed Mose. "Ha, ha!"

"It got out of my pocket some way," said George, "and I forgot it. Then a minute ago I

Then suddenly George went to the chair and put his hand under
the seat.

saw the tip of its tail and I remembered. They knock with their tails."

"Knock! Knock!" teased Mose. "Spirits, Sue, spirits!"

"George Carver, if you ever bring any more of your pets into this house, I'll give you a good licking."

"Yes, ma'am," smiled George.

3. Flowers and Pods

George was eight years old now but he was small for his age. He was so thin he could slip through a crack—if he could get his head through.

He had never been strong like Jim. That whooping cough and the long cold ride to Arkansas had left him weak and sickly.

He couldn't do any hard work but he did the outside chores. He brought water from the spring. He picked up chips, gathered eggs, carried in wood, pulled weeds, cut grass, planted seeds and hoed a little.

Every day, unless it was raining, he went to the woods. There was so much to see there even in the winter.

There were always pretty pebbles and rocks

He was so thin he could slip through a crack—if he could get his head through.

along the creek. He filled his pockets with them and carried them home. He had a pile of them now by the front doorstep.

In the spring he picked the lovely forest flowers—purple violets, wild sweet Williams and pinkish-white spring beauties.

He was delighted when the fence corners were filled with those tall weeds with their lacy flowers.

He was delighted also when thistles bloomed. His fingers were pricked from pulling their lovely purple flowers but he didn't care.

He filled his pockets with pods and seeds. He would go to sleep at night holding some blossom or pod in his hand.

Mrs. Carver didn't like the mess they made but she didn't say anything. That is, not till one morning. Even then, it was Jim who complained.

He had got up early, before George was awake. Of course Mr. and Mrs. Carver were up.

They always got up at four o'clock winter and summer.

"I couldn't sleep last night," Jim said. "Something bit me, I guess—my back is sore."

"It might have been a spider," said Sue.

"There's lots of scorpions around now," said Mose. "I'd better go up and see."

One look at the bed and the sleeping boy was enough. George held a thistle pod in one hand.

"That's what bit you, Jim."

So George was told to keep his pods and flowers out of bed. "You can bring them into the house," Sue said, "but you cannot take them to the loft."

4. Milkweed Fluff

That fall, stalks of milkweed stood in each corner of the big kitchen. It was almost time for the pods to open and George wanted to save the soft fluff that filled them. He thought he'd use it some way. He didn't know just how but maybe he could find a way.

"George," said Mrs. Carver one night, "please get this milkweed out of here. The leaves have dried and they're all over the floor."

"I'll take them out tomorrow morning, Miss Sue." But he forgot and went to the pasture with Jim.

Mrs. Carver forgot them herself, she was so busy making jelly and getting dinner. She hadn't noticed that the milkweed pods had burst open.

Suddenly the kitchen was filled with flying fluff. A thousand little brown seeds with their white silken sails were blowing everywhere.

They fell into a dish of stewed corn. They plastered the meat and the dish of butter. They fell into gravy, milk, cream and applesauce.

Worst of all was the jelly. It was boiling hard so of course it boiled the fluff along with the juice. The seeds and fibers were mixed all through it. Mrs. Carver had to throw it out.

She tried to save the food. She picked and

The milkweed pods had burst open. Suddenly the kitchen was filled with flying fluff.

skimmed and scraped and strained. She finally saved most of it and called Mose to dinner.

"You're late today, Sue. Did things go wrong?"

By the time Susan Carver had finished telling

what was wrong, a certain little Negro boy just about knew what would happen next.

And it did. "George Carver, it's all your fault. March yourself out to the woodshed. Jim, get me a good strong switch."

"No, Sue," said Mose. "It wasn't the boy's fault the pods all opened at once and a wind was blowing."

"Well, I suppose it wasn't. I won't punish you this time, George, but it better not happen again. Do you hear that, George?"

"Yes, ma'am."

III

THE PLANT DOCTOR

1. Jim Worries about George

JIM CARVER was worried. His handsome face was sad. His eyes were dull. He walked slower. He didn't sleep well. He didn't eat half as much. He didn't laugh at all.

He worked with Mr. Carver every day, for he was eleven years old now and he was big and strong. He was a good worker; he didn't have to be told twice how to do a thing.

At least, that's the way it had been. Now, however, for the last week Jim had to be told two or three times. But Moses didn't scold the boy. He thought he'd get over it in a day or two, whatever it was.

Jim didn't get over it; he was even worse.

Then Moses asked him what he was worrying about.

"It's George, Marse Mose. He ain't acting right. He won't go fishing with me or hunting neither. He just goes off alone to the woods."

"You know why he goes there, Jim. It's his garden."

"I know it, but what does he want a garden away off in the woods for? Can't he plant his flowers in the yard? Miss Sue said he could."

"Yes, but she wouldn't like piles of clay and sand in the yard. She wouldn't like it mixed with the soil."

"Does he have to mix it?"

"Different kinds of flowers need different kinds of soil. Besides, there's no one to bother George out in the woods. The schoolboys can't run over it; they don't even know where it is. And George doesn't want them to know."

"What makes George like that, Marse Mose?"

"I can't tell you that, Jim; it puzzles me. I never knew a boy like him. He'd rather work with his plants than eat."

"I thought maybe he was wrong in his head."

"No indeed! He's smart; he notices everything. If I move a peg in the barn, he'll know it."

Jim felt better now. Marse Mose knew pretty much everything. He was the best farmer in the county and he raised the best race horses. He trained them, too, and sold them for a good price.

At every big fair in Missouri there were sure to be some of Mose Carver's horses in the races.

"So he ought to know about George," Jim said to himself.

2. The Secret Garden

George was doing strange things in his secret garden. He planted some of his flowers in clay, some in sand and some in loam, the rich black soil of the woods.

Then he watched them carefully to see how they grew. After a while he dug them up and looked at their roots. If these didn't look healthy he re-planted them in different soil and watched them again.

He kept on changing them until he found the kind of soil that kind of plant needed.

For a month now he had watched some petunias. He had planted them in the loam but they hadn't done well. First they became pale. Then they withered and some died.

George knew then that he had made a wonderful discovery. The petunias had eaten too much rich food! They couldn't digest it—it killed them.

"They're just like people," he told Jim. "If we eat too much cake we get sick."

He dug up the petunias and planted them in mixed soil, clay and loam. Then he watched them closely. Would their dry brown stalks turn green? Would new leaves come out? Would buds appear?

He thought there had been a change yesterday. He'd be sure of it today. He was anxious to get to his garden to see.

The wood box was filled early. The water was carried in. The chickens were fed and the eggs gathered. Now George was on his way to the woods.

He had crossed the barnyard when he heard Mrs. Carver call him. He could pretend he didn't hear her. He was out of sight; she'd never know.

But George was honest. He never told lies and he didn't act them, either.

Mrs. Carver said one day that she'd believe red was green if George said it was.

Mr. Carver laughed and said he'd believe the colt was a calf if George said so.

So George turned and went back toward the cabin.

3. An Unwelcome Visitor

George wondered what Miss Sue wanted. His chores were all done. Then suddenly he knew and his heart was like lead.

At the hitching post near the house was Lynn Wilson's pony. And there was Lynn sitting on the doorstep.

He was a nephew of Mr. Carver and was the same age as George. But he was large and strong and rough.

He thought it was great fun to throw George down and roll him over and over. He made fun of him because he was undersized and weak. George dreaded his visits.

"Hurry up!" called Lynn. "I want to see your garden!"

George was so surprised he couldn't say anything.

"Well, come on! What are you waiting for?"

"I didn't know you knew——"

"I told him, George," said Mrs. Carver from the door. "It's all right—it's all in the family. His mother wants him to make a garden like yours."

George didn't answer for a minute. He was thinking of that pile of pretty stones he had made by the doorstep. He remembered how Lynn had thrown them all away, just for fun. He had begged him to leave some but Lynn had only laughed at him.

He knew what Lynn would do to his garden. He'd pull up plants, just for fun. He'd trample on them, just for fun. Then he'd roll George over the beds. That would be for fun, too.

All this flashed through his mind and he knew he couldn't show his garden to this bully. He wouldn't—no one could make him.

"No," he said at last, "I—I can't."

"Make him, Aunt Sue!" Lynn demanded. "Tell him he has to! He's nothing but a slave!"

"See here, Lynn Wilson," said Susan Carver sharply, "don't call George a slave. Don't you know the war is over? Don't you know the Negroes have been freed?"

"Pooh! My folks say we don't have to pay any attention to that out here in Missouri."

"Your folks are wrong. We do have to pay attention; it's the law. George and Jim are as free as you are. They can leave us any time."

"Well, anyway, I want to see his garden."

Mrs. Carver looked at George. She saw that he was suffering. He looked sick.

"Lynn," she said, "George can't take you there today. Wait till your mother can come with you." Then she went into the house and closed the door.

"Come on!" Lynn said. "If you don't I'll find out where it is and I'll pull up every flower in it."

"Don't you dare!" cried George. "Don't you dare to touch my flowers!"

"I don't care what you say. I can throw you with one hand."

"Better not try it," said Jim's voice. Then Jim himself came from around the house. "You'll have to throw me first," he went on.

"Oh, I was just teasing him. He's too touchy about his garden."

"Well, it's his. Marse Mose gave him the ground."

Then Lynn jumped on his pony and rode away.

"All right, I wouldn't look at it now. You couldn't make me." Then Lynn jumped on his pony and rode away.

George hurried into the woods. In a few minutes he was looking at the petunias. They were stronger! A tiny bit of green showed in their stems!

No, it just wouldn't do to give plants too much rich food. Not unless you wanted to kill them.

4. George's Plant Hospital

As the weeks went by, George learned more and more about plants. He found that some grew better in the shade while others needed the sun.

He found that some must be soaked with water while others needed very little.

He learned how to get rid of the worms that cut the roots. He learned what to do when rust withered the leaves.

The news got around the Diamond Grove

neighborhood that George had a way with flowers. And now the neighbors were bringing him their plants to doctor.

Mrs. May brought a geranium that was turning yellow. Mrs. Perry brought a rose that had wilted. Mrs. Baynham brought a fern that was dying.

Mrs. McMurty brought a plant that wouldn't bloom. Mrs. Olsen brought a vine that wouldn't grow. Other ladies brought other flowers and vines.

George now called his garden a hospital. And no doctor ever watched his sick patients closer than he watched his sick plants. He usually cured them, too.

The ladies called him their "Plant Doctor," and George was delighted. So was Jim. So were Mr. and Mrs. Carver.

Then one day Mrs. Wilson and Lynn came.

They came to his garden, too, and no one else ever did that.

No doctor ever watched his sick patients closer than George watched his sick plants.

"You must show Lynn how you cure plants," said Mrs. Wilson. "I want him to doctor mine."

"You'll have to pay me," growled Lynn.

"Of course I will, dear. How did you learn all this, George?"

"I watched the plants growing."

"I'm not going to sit around and watch a lot of old plants grow."

"You don't need to, darling. George will tell you everything. Now I'm going to see Aunt Sue. Come up to the house when you're through."

"Well, go on, George," ordered Lynn as soon as his mother had disappeared. "Tell me." Then he began to kick at the rocks around the flower beds.

George had spent a good deal of time getting these rocks. He knew where each one came from and how they were marked.

"Don't do that!" he cried angrily. "Let those rocks alone!"

Lynn laughed and went on kicking them.

George was helpless. He could only stand there and watch.

Then out of the brush stepped Mr. Moses Carver. He appeared so suddenly and so quietly Lynn didn't see him.

"Pick up every one of those rocks and put them back in the border," said Mr. Carver sharply.

"Yes, sir." Lynn picked up the rocks and put them back.

"Now then," said Moses, "go to your mother. And don't you come to this garden again."

"Yes, sir."

Lynn went and he went quickly, too. Moses Carver wasn't the kind of a man anyone would disobey.

"I love you, Marse Mose," said George.

Moses took the boy's thin little hand in his.

"I love you, child," he said. "You're a good boy, a mighty good boy."

IV

STRAWBERRIES, SCHOOL, SPELLER

1. At the County Fair

"THERE never were such strawberries anywhere else on earth," said Mr. Carl Bruder. "Missouri's got the whole world beat."

"It's the truth you're speaking," said Mr. Pat O'Connor, "but you've only told the half of it. Our Diamond Grove berries are the best in Missouri."

"That's not all of it, either," added Mr. Baynham. "Moses Carver's berries are the best in Diamond Grove."

All three gentlemen laughed. They were looking at the fruit exhibit at the County Fair and they had just come to a large basket of strawberries. They now read the name of the grower on a tag.

"Moses Carver!" they exclaimed.

"Look at them!" Mr. Baynham cried. "Prettiest things I ever saw—every berry perfect!"

"Look at the size of them!" exclaimed Pat. "If they're not as big as pigeon eggs then I wasn't born in Ireland."

"I've eaten Mose's berries many a time," bragged Carl. "They're so sweet they don't need sugar."

"They smell sweet," declared Mr. Baynham. "Do you notice that fragrance? Was there ever anything more delicious?"

"How does Mose get such berries?" asked Mr. O'Connor. "My soil is as good as his but I can't raise berries like these."

"No one can," Mr. Bruder said. "Mose seems to know things the rest of us don't know."

Two colored boys heard every word of this. They were lying on the grass close by and couldn't help hearing. Now they were nudging each other and grinning.

They knew all about the Carver berries. Didn't they help raise them and pick them? Didn't they eat them every day now, with cream and sugar? They didn't agree with Mr. Bruder on that point, they whispered.

Now the men were talking again and once more the boys heard them plainly.

"Moses will make money on his berries this year," said Carl.

"I wish I knew how he does it," said Pat.

"Maybe little George tells him how," said Mr. Baynham smiling.

The others smiled. They knew all about George and his garden.

"Well," said Carl, "that boy does know a lot about plants and soil. It's a pity he can't go to school and study such things."

"He'd have to learn to read first," said Pat.

"And how's he going to do that? This Diamond Grove school is for white children only."

"I know," nodded Mr. Baynham, "and it's too bad, it is indeed. He'd be a wonder in that line if he had an education."

Then the gentlemen moved on and the boys jumped up and looked at each other gravely. They had always known they couldn't go to school so they hadn't thought much about it. But now, in the last five minutes, things had changed.

"Mr. Bruder said I ought to study about plants," said George.

"Mr. O'Connor said you'd have to learn to read first. And how can you, George? They won't let us go to school."

"Why won't they? They let us go to the church for white folks. They ask us to come."

"I can't understand, never could."

—"I want to go to school! I've got to go to school, Jim!"

Jim shook his head. "Looks like learning is only for the white folks."

"I'll ask Marse Mose to talk to the teacher."

"It wouldn't do any good. If you went the white children would leave."

George's voice trembled. "Because I'm black?"

Jim nodded. "You've got to get used to that."

"But the white boys play with me! They come to see us!"

"I know they do, but school is different somehow."

Then George cried and he cried so hard Jim couldn't stop him.

"Hush, honey," Jim said. "Hush, honey," he said again and again.

After a while George stopped, but the Fair wasn't any fun now so they went back home.

2. On the Schoolhouse Steps

The Diamond Grove school was about two miles from the Carver farm. It was a log house with only one room, and it stood in a field that wasn't used. The land was worn out. The woods were just back of it and there wasn't a house in sight.

The door was closed today, for the air was chilly. So no one saw the thin little Negro boy who sat shivering on the log doorstep.

George had gone there because he couldn't stay away. He wanted to know how it would feel to be so close to a schoolroom.

He could hear the murmur of voices inside and he longed to know what they were saying.

Why couldn't he know? Why couldn't he go inside? It wasn't his fault his skin was black. God made him black.

Mr. Carver said that last night. And he said

No one saw the thin little Negro boy who sat shivering on the log doorstep.

he wished George could go to school; he'd be glad to buy his books. And Mrs. Carver said he'd be at the head of his class in no time.

Then George remembered how Mr. Carver shook his head when he asked him to talk to the teacher. It was just as Jim said.

Young as he was, he understood. He'd never have a chance to be anybody. He'd be shut out of things. He cried a long time that night up in the loft, and Jim didn't try to stop him.

Tears filled his eyes now as he thought of it. The next minute he was sobbing.

He was afraid they'd hear him in the school, so he ran. He ran straight to the only place he always felt safe—his garden in the woods.

When he reached it he knelt down and prayed. He prayed out loud and he prayed with all his might.

"Dear Lord, please let me go to school! I

want to read and write. Dear Lord, please fix it so I can learn! Please, please fix it, dear Lord!"

3. The Blue-Backed Speller

George felt better now. He firmly believed the Lord would answer his prayer. So he hurried home. He always helped Miss Sue get dinner; he didn't want to be late.

She was teaching him to cook and he liked it. She had already taught him to clean the house and make the beds. He liked that work, too. He was quick about it and as neat as a girl.

He had learned to knit just by watching Mrs. Carver. He thought he could learn to patch and mend by watching her. But that didn't work. She didn't like his stitches.

"Too long," she said. She kept on saying it until he learned to make them short, very, very short. Then she was pleased.

George was smiling as he entered the kitchen. "Am I late?" he asked.

"No, I'm not ready to begin dinner yet but I will be pretty soon."

"I went to the schoolhouse."

"Oh!" exclaimed Mrs. Carver. "That makes me think of something!"

She took a blue-backed book from the table and handed it to George. "Here's a speller for you. I found it in an old trunk this morning."

"Do you mean it's mine?"

"Of course; I'm giving it to you. Now you can learn to spell and read."

"Read! But it's a speller——"

"There's reading in it, plenty of reading. Look! And here's a page that shows how to write."

"Why, it's the same as going to school, Miss Sue! I'll learn to spell and read and write!"

The child was so delighted he stood on his

head. He turned somersaults. He giggled and sang and whistled.

He took the speller out to the barn to show to Mr. Carver and Jim. It was a wonder book. Fairyland itself couldn't have been more beautiful than this old speller.

It was so precious he took it to bed with him and put it under his pillow.

That night Sue was telling Moses how she found the speller. "It's queer, I had forgotten the book; I hadn't seen it in years. All of a sudden this morning I thought of it. I tried to remember where it was but I couldn't. So I gave up and went on about my work.

"But I kept seeing that book! There it was right before my eyes."

"Spirits, Sue," teased Mose.

Sue smiled. "Well, suddenly I remembered. I went straight to that old trunk and there it was!"

"Well, well!" said Moses. "It was queer."

George didn't think it was queer. That night he knelt by his bed and prayed aloud just as he had in the woods.

"Dear Lord, I thank Thee for the speller. I'm going to study hard so you won't be sorry you sent it. Maybe I can get Jim to study it, too. Amen."

"Amen!" said Jim softly from the bed.

4. George Surprises Everyone

It was winter now and George couldn't work with his plants. So he put all his spare time on his speller.

In a month or so he knew his ABC's. In another month or so he could spell a few words and read some short sentences. In another two months he could read Mother Goose rhymes.

"It beats anything I ever saw, the way that boy learns," declared Mr. Carver.

"I never saw anyone learn so fast in all my life," declared Mrs. Carver.

George studied and studied. Every chance he had he studied. Mrs. Carver helped him with his spelling and reading and writing.

Mr. Carver taught him arithmetic. He was learning the multiplication tables now. He'd say them to anyone who would listen.

It was surprising how many did listen. George didn't know he had so many good friends. There were the neighbors. There were the ladies whose plants he had cured. There were the minister and the doctor and some horse-buyers. Then there were Mr. Carl Bruder and Mr. Pat O'Connor and Mr. Baynham. All of them said they couldn't do better themselves.

At the end of six months George read a book by himself. The Carvers were so proud of him they told the neighbors.

Before long this news had traveled up and

down the creeks, over the hills and into the valleys. Everyone was glad to hear it.

They lent their books to George. They told him of books he ought to read.

They also told their own children it was a pity they couldn't be more like George Carver and study the way he did.

V

HOW GEORGE SAVED HIS FRIEND

1. Rosie

WINTER was still here and George was lonesome. He couldn't study all the time. He couldn't work in his garden. He didn't have anyone to play with. Jim was busy all day and Mr. Carver was away most of the time, taking his horses to fairs.

Well, he had one good friend anyway—Rosie, a two-year-old filly and a beauty. She was coal-black and had a white star on her forehead.

She would race across the pasture when George whistled. She'd nose about in his pockets till she found the sugar he always brought.

She would lay her head on his shoulder and nuzzle up to his neck. George would pet her and sing softly to her. He always sang the same song because she whinnied the first time he sang it.

Sometimes she would show off for him. She'd run fast and stop short. She'd trot and pace and rack and gallop. She'd stand on her hind legs and snort.

Rosie would stand on her hind legs and snort. George would almost die laughing.

George would almost die laughing. He said she knew he was laughing at her capers and she laughed herself.

"Horses can't laugh," said Jim.

"Rosie can," George insisted. "She throws back her head, and draws back her lips and shows her teeth. Of course she's laughing."

Every time George left her she would stand at the fence looking after him. She'd whinny, too, as long as she could see him.

After a while Moses noticed this and was displeased, very displeased.

"How long have you been petting that horse?" he asked sharply.

"Not very long—a month or so."

"You ought to know better you've been around horses enough."

"I didn't think she'd be like other horses. She's so much smarter. She's Pacer's granddaughter."

"They're all alike. If they get used to something you can't do a thing with them. I remember a horse I used to own. She had a rooster for a pet."

George laughed. "What made her take up with a rooster?"

"He had been sleeping in her stall every night, so when I took her to the races she missed the bird. She was stubborn and mean. She wouldn't even try to run. She just bucked and kicked. Finally I had to send for that rooster and put him in her stall."

"Did she run then?"

"Like a streak, and took the prize."

"Do you think Rosie will miss me?"

"I'm afraid of it. And I can't take you around to the races with her. So, no more petting."

"Yes, sir. But she won't understand it."

George looked so sad Moses felt sorry for him. "I'm sorry," he said, "but that's the way I make my living."

2. Queenie

Rosie was gone by the time George was up the next morning. Mr. Carver had taken her to a race at a county fair.

The pasture looked lonesome without her. He was lonesome himself. He didn't know what to do.

Late that afternoon he went to the dog kennel and looked at the bloodhounds. There were twelve of them in a high pen. George wished he could let them out and play with them, but he couldn't. Mr. Carver wouldn't allow that.

He kept them for fox hunting. It would ruin them to pet them.

"If you pet a hunting dog," Mr. Carver said, "he won't be any account. He won't work. He'll hunt a little while, then he'll quit and run back home to be petted."

The dogs didn't bark at George because they knew him; he helped Jim feed them. But if a stranger came they barked so fiercely it was frightful to hear. Mrs. Carver said it always scared her—away up at the cabin.

Then George saw one of the hounds, Queenie, in a pen by herself with her six pups. And before

George saw one of the hounds, Queenie, in a pen by herself with her six puppies.

he knew what he was doing he was down on his knees outside the pen.

He just had to pet them, they were so cute and pretty. And to his surprise Queenie put her head down to be rubbed.

Suddenly there stood Moses Carver! George jumped to his feet. He knew what was coming.

"I told you not to pet the hounds," said Mr. Carver angrily.

"I'm sorry, sir, I forgot. The pups looked so cute—and Queenie put her head down— and——"

"That's no excuse," Mose interrupted. "You have disobeyed me and I shall punish you. You'll have no supper and you will sleep in the hayloft tonight."

"Yes, sir."

"Go up there now and stay there."

George went up the straight ladder and into the loft. He was glad Mr. Carver didn't believe in whipping. He'd rather sleep in the hayloft, even if he was all alone.

This was his first time, but Jim had spent several nights here. George didn't think he'd be afraid. Jim said he wasn't.

He made a hole in the hay and curled up in it. Then he thought things over. Of course Mr. Carver was right. You had to get rid of foxes or you wouldn't have any chickens or ducks or geese.

He was right about Queenie, too. He had spent weeks training her to trail foxes. It was hard work—out in all kinds of weather, up hill and down hill, through mud and briers— briers——

George was getting sleepy now. The words just trailed along in his mind—"briers—briers— briers——"

Then George was asleep.

3. Horse Thieves

George didn't know when he went to sleep.

But he knew when he woke up—suddenly—sometime in the night. He heard voices, and light showed through cracks in the loft floor.

Men were talking in the barn just below him. George thought that one of the horses was sick and Mr. Carver and Jim were taking care of it.

There must be some neighbors, too, for he heard several voices. He listened for a minute or so, but he didn't hear Mr. Carver or Jim. That was strange—he'd take a look.

As softly as a cat, George crept to the edge of the loft and looked down. Then he saw a sight that frightened him.

Several men stood around a lighted lantern on the floor. The boy knew they were horse thieves the minute he saw them. They were rough and mean-looking.

One man was going from stall to stall. Another man came in through the open door.

"Ten horses here," said the first man.

"Five out in the pasture," said the second.

"Don't want 'em," declared the leader. "It takes too long to round 'em up. Get these ready to travel, and be quick about it."

George's heart almost stopped beating. "They'll get Rosie—they'll whip her—they'll dig their spurs into her sides," he said to himself.

He was frantic. He must save Rosie—he must —he must! He was thinking fast. What could he do? What? What?

Then he thought of the bloodhounds. Yes! Yes! That was the way! He'd get to their pen. He'd free them. They'd scare the thieves away. He'd do it if they shot him.

He crept to a side wall and found a wide crack between two boards. He squeezed through and dropped to the ground. Then he ran to the kennels.

He opened Queenie's pen first and let her out.

Then he opened the gate to the big pen and out rushed the twelve bloodhounds.

George ran toward the barn. The hounds ran after him, barking and baying.

"Bloodhounds!" yelled the leader. "Run!" The men ran for their lives. They jumped on their horses and galloped away.

George now turned and ran toward the cabin. The hounds ran after him. He didn't think they would attack him but he wasn't sure. They were excited and they were barking fiercely.

He was running now like a streak of lightning. If he could only climb a tree! But there wasn't any tree, not till he got close to the cabin. Could he outrun them that far?

Then out of the darkness came a light. And out of the silence of the night came voices—Jim's and Mr. Carver's.

"Help! Help!" cried George.

Jim quieted the dogs and took them back to the pen.

George told Mr. Carver about the thieves and how he had tried to save the horses.

"You're a brave boy," said Mr. Carver. "You shall have a horse of your own for this. You shall have Rosie."

"Rosie! Do you mean you are giving her to me—to keep—for my own?"

"For your own. You've earned her by your bravery."

There wasn't a happier boy in the world this night, not in the whole wide world.

He didn't finish the night in the hayloft, either. And he ate his supper, too, and an extra good one.

VI

STRANGE THINGS HAD HAPPENED

1. On the Road to Neosho

GEORGE was on his way to Neosho, a little town eight miles from Diamond Grove. And strange to say, George was walking. He, the owner of a fine race horse, was walking! He was barefoot, too!

Another strange thing: George carried all of his clothing, except what he wore, in a little bundle.

But the strangest thing of all was this: He had left his home—the only home he had ever known. He was going out into the world alone so he could go to school.

He was only ten years old. He was an orphan. He didn't know anyone in Neosho.

Worse still, he didn't know how he'd get food

or where he would sleep. He had no money and he had no work.

George was on his way to Neosho. He had left his home—the only home he had ever known.

—But there was something he did have and plenty of it, too—*courage*. He didn't even think of turning back.

He was determined to find work so he could make his living and buy his schoolbooks.

He had been walking since sunup and he was

tired. The road was hilly and rough. He had to rest often.

It was noon now and he sat under a tree to eat his lunch of fat pork and cornbread.

He should be on his way but he had so much to think about. He'd sit here a little longer.

He thought of the things that had happened since the night he saved the horses, just two weeks ago.

The thieves had come back in the daytime. Two of them had held guns over Mr. Carver and Jim. The others had rounded up the cattle and horses.

He remembered how they drove them over the strawberry beds and ruined the berry crop. He had watched them from the hayloft where he was hiding.

He saw them tip over the beehives and gallop their horses over the vegetable garden and tear down the grapevines.

"It was just pure meanness," George said aloud, "just pure meanness."

So in about one hour the Carvers had lost everything but their land.

Moses couldn't even pay Jim his wages, but that loyal boy was staying anyway for a while.

In fact Moses Carver couldn't do anything he had planned; that new room for the log cabin—that new dress for his wife—the new chicken house—the new crib for corn—the new feed trough—the new fence.

Everything had to be given up, even the plans he had made for sending George to school in Neosho.

A school for colored children had just been started there and George was to ride Rosie back and forth.

But now there was no Rosie and not a cent for schoolbooks.

"I can go anyway," George had said. "I can find work. I'll cook for some lady."

Mrs. Carver shook her head. "You can't cook anything but boiled dinners and stews, George. Townfolks want pie and cake."

"Well then, I'll cut grass and run errands and sweep stores. There's lots of things I can do."

At last the Carvers consented. They said George must come back if he couldn't find work. And Jim said he'd come to see him every Saturday afternoon. So it wasn't like going away for good.

He was rested now and again on his way. He had expected to be in Neosho by this time. He had stopped too often.

It was almost dark when he reached the town. It was too late to look for work. It was even too late to run an errand for his supper. He had to look for a place to sleep.

He found an old barn at the edge of town and

climbed to the loft. He was hungry but he was too tired to think much about it.

He snuggled down into the hay and was asleep in two minutes.

2. On the Woodpile

Early the next morning George came out of the barn and looked about. He was in the back yard of a neat little place.

A small trim house faced the street. No grass grew in the walk around the house. There was no trash in the back yard. There was no pile of ashes anywhere. The wood was stacked evenly in a pile. There was a neat bed of flowers.

"I can't get work here," he thought. "Everything's been done."

There was no one about, so he sat on the woodpile to think it over. "I'll have to get some food," he said to himself. "My stomach's all caved in.

Wonder where I'd better go first for work—to the stores or to houses?"

The back door opened and out came a nice-looking Negro woman. She was neat, too—as neat as the house and yard.

She came straight to the woodpile and then she saw George.

"Good morning," she said with a smile.

"Good morning," said George, and smiled back. He jumped down quickly and took off his hat. Miss Sue had taught him good manners.

"What are you doing here so early, child? Did you come to school before breakfast?"

She waved her hand toward a little house next door. George looked and smiled again.

"Oh! Is that the school—the Negro school?"

The woman was puzzled. "Aren't you one of the pupils?" she asked.

George told her everything and Mrs. Watkins

The back door opened and out came a nice-looking Negro woman.

listened and asked questions. When he was through she pointed to his little bundle.

"Did you bring all your clothes?"

"Yes, ma'am. It's all I own. It's my Sunday shirt—it's ruffled."

"That's very nice," said the woman kindly. "Now you come in and eat breakfast with us. My husband hasn't gone to work yet."

George went into one of the cleanest, tidiest little houses he had ever seen. There were growing plants, too   noticed them the first thing.

Mr. Andrew Watkins was friendly with George even before he heard his story. Afterward, he took the boy's hand and held it tightly and said he was glad he had come to their barn.

"He can cook, Andy," said Mariah.

"Plain cooking," added George quickly, "boiled dinners and stews. I can make pancakes pretty good, too."

"That's just what we like," said Andy. "Better get him to stay with us, Mariah."

Mariah turned to George. "I'm a nurse," she said, "and I have to be away a good deal. Could you get Andy's meals?"

"Of course. I can do the washings, too. And I'll mend his clothes and patch them."

"Why, he'll take care of me, Mariah," said good-natured Andy.

"But I'll have to go to school," said George. "I can work before and after."

"Of course you'll go to school," said Andy— "just the same as if you were our own son."

"Of course," said Mariah.

"I didn't dream I'd be so lucky," said the boy gratefully.

"It's not luck," said Mariah firmly. "God led you here and sat you on that woodpile so I could see you and take you in."

VII

GEORGE'S FIRST SCHOOL

1. Not a Minute Wasted

GEORGE wanted to enter school that afternoon but Mariah Watkins wouldn't hear of it. His clothes would have to be washed and ironed and he would need a good rest.

The next morning George was as neat as a pin and he felt rested and strong. But when he entered the schoolhouse his legs were weak; he was weak all over. He was actually going into a schoolroom!

"Have you ever gone to school?" asked the young Negro teacher.

"N-n-o, s-sir," answered George with a trembling voice.

"You needn't worry about that. You'll get used to it in three or four days."

"Why!" the teacher exclaimed. "I

thought you had never gone to school."

The teacher was a kind young man. He knew how shy boys were in their first school. So he didn't ask George to do anything for almost a week.

He had put him in the primary class with the beginners. "On Friday," he thought, "I'll start him on his ABC's."

On Friday morning before school began, he heard George reading aloud to some boys. He was surprised. "Why!" he exclaimed. "I thought you had never gone to school."

"I didn't, sir. I learned to read from a speller."

The teacher had two more surprises when he heard him spell and say his tables. When George left that afternoon he was in the Third Grade.

How that boy studied! Not a minute was wasted. He was determined to keep up with his class. It was hard because he had to make his living at the same time.

He got up at daylight to help Mariah. He helped after school. He even went home at recess to help. Then back, over the fence, to school again.

Not a minute was wasted. He even went home at recess to help Mariah.

The teacher was pleased. "I've never seen a boy who wanted so much to learn," he said.

Mr. and Mrs. Watkins were pleased with George, also. He was such a help to them. He was quiet about the house and polite. He was neat in his own room and kept his clothing clean.

So, with two good friends, a roof over his head, three meals every day and his school, George should have been happy.

2. *Mariah Plays Detective*

George *was* happy for a time. Then came a change. He didn't complain about anything but he wasn't lively. He didn't sing or laugh. He didn't tell what went on at school.

"Something's wrong," Andy said for the tenth time.

"I know it," agreed Mariah, "but I can't figure out what it is."

They knew he wasn't homesick for his brother,

for Jim came to see him every Saturday afternoon.

He had seen the Carvers, too. He had spent last Sunday with them and had gone to church.

"I can't figure it out," Mariah said again. "I guess I'll just watch and see what's going on in that schoolyard."

She began then to play detective. She looked over the fence; she peeped through the cracks between the boards. In two days she knew what was wrong.

She asked George that evening why the boys didn't let him play with them.

George was embarrassed. "They asked me at first, Aunt Mariah."

"I saw them shoving you around. I didn't like the way they treated you. I've a good notion to tell them so."

"No! No! Please don't! It isn't their fault. I wouldn't play with them."

"Why wouldn't you?"

George was silent for a moment. Then he burst out: "I can't! I'm a runt! They hurt me!"

Mariah's kind heart was touched. She understood now. George was ashamed of his weak little body. He was ashamed because he couldn't play rough games.

"Don't you mind, honey child!" she said gently. "You know more than all the rest of them put together."

"They don't care about that," said George sadly.

"I'll fix them. I'll make them look up to you. See if I don't."

Every day after that George saw Mrs. Watkins talking to some boy over the fence—a different boy each time. He wondered what she said but she wouldn't tell. The boys didn't tell him, either.

At the end of the week there was a change.

The boys had quit teasing him and shoving him about. They began to play marbles and mumblety-peg and they asked him to play with them.

Now there was a change in George. He laughed and joked and talked about school. He sang over the washtub. He sang over the ironing board. George was himself again.

Then Mrs. Watkins told what she had said.

"I made 'em think you were something extra special, George. I told them you were the only boy in the world that ever got away from Night Riders. And I said you had to be extra special or Mr. Carver wouldn't have given up a fine race horse to get you back."

George laughed. "Well anyway, I've won all their marbles. And none of them can flip a knife the way I do in mumblety-peg."

"It's your fingers, boy," said Andy. "You can do anything with 'em. Never saw the likes of it—

never in all my life. I'd say you *are* 'extra special'."

3. *Things George Could Do*

A year had passed. George was still with the Watkins family. He was still doing good work in school. He was still using his wonderful hands: he was doing odd jobs all over town.

Mariah had taught him to do fancy cooking—pies, cakes, meat roasts and breads.

She was a fine cook herself but it wasn't long before George's biscuits were better than hers. His salt-rising bread was better, for it was *always* good.

He knitted socks for Andy and he knitted his own. He made rag rugs for Mariah. He crocheted collars and cuffs for neighbors.

He could go to a store, see a set of crocheted collars and cuffs, come home and copy them. He could remember the pattern no matter how difficult. Sometimes he made up his own patterns.

The neighbors thought he ought to make his living this way. But George always shook his head. He was going to teach Negro boys and girls who had never had a chance to study. He was going to teach school, he said, just as soon as he was through high school.

He had one pupil, however, much sooner—his brother. Jim came to Neosho to find work and go to school. And while he was saving money to buy books, George taught him his ABC's.

He was teaching him to read when something happened that scared them all—Andy, Mariah, Jim, the teacher and the neighbors.

George was sick, sick in bed, too, for a week or so. Then he was up and about but not strong enough to go to school.

Some said he had been working too hard. Others said he needed a cooler climate. They said Kansas would be better for him than Missouri.

At last they all decided that George should go to Kansas.

VIII

GEORGE GOES TO KANSAS

1. The Wagon Ride

A NEGRO family was moving from Neosho to Fort Scott, Kansas. They had a small wagon drawn by two mules and in this wagon was everything they owned—furniture, bedding, clothing, tools and a coop with chickens.

The Smiths and their two small children sat in the driver's seat. On top of the piled-up furniture and household goods sat George. He also was moving to Fort Scott.

The road was hilly and George had to hold on to something every time the wagon went downhill. It was even worse going up for there was the danger of sliding off.

Between hills he had time to think. He thought of his last visit to Diamond Grove to tell the

Carvers good-by. He thought of Aunt Mariah's prayer last night.

She had asked the Lord to look after him and see that he had a place to sleep and food to eat and work to do.

On top of the piled-up furniture and household goods sat George.

George smiled as he remembered the last part. "Get him a good school, Lord. And, O dear Lord, get him a teacher who knows enough to teach him, for that boy is mighty smart."

He smiled again as he thought of how Jim had promised to write him as soon as he learned how. Of course he had promised to write Jim. The boys loved each other dearly and they intended to live together just as soon as one was settled. Jim said he'd go to Fort Scott if George liked it there.

Then the wagon almost tipped over. The goods almost fell out and George almost fell off.

From then on he had no time to think. The road had deep ruts and the wagon was forever tipping this way or that. George had to hang on for dear life.

He was always glad when they stopped to eat. He was thankful when night came and he could roll up in a blanket and stretch out on the ground to sleep. It was a hard bed but better than pitching forward and falling backward all day long.

There were three days of this before they reached Fort Scott. As it was getting dark

George thanked his friends and looked for a place to sleep.

He found a barn at the edge of town, squeezed through a wide crack and slept in the hayloft.

2. No Grass Grew under George's Feet

In the morning George was out early looking for work. He swept a store to earn his breakfast; he milked a cow to earn his dinner; he brushed a horse to earn his supper. That night he slept in the barn again.

The next day he found a school for Negro children and talked with the teacher. The books he had brought from Neosho wouldn't do, she said. He'd have to buy new books.

That meant George couldn't enter now. He'd have to wait till he had saved three dollars.

By evening he was working for Mrs. Simms, the cooper's wife. He was to take care of her two little children after school, and on Saturdays and Sundays.

He slept in a tiny room back of the kitchen. The narrow bed was hard as a rock and the covers were old and thin.

He had to wash outside in the yard and take his bath in the woodshed.

Sometimes his food was what was left after the family had eaten. Mostly he had turnip greens and fat pork, or just cornbread and molasses.

Mr. and Mrs. Simms didn't think they were mistreating George. They had always treated their help this way.

Of course George didn't like all this; he didn't like any part of it. But what could he do? Regular work was hard to get, and he must go to school.

School—that was the main thing. He would stand anything for that. So he did stand it and before a month passed he had earned his book money and was in school.

The Simmses' children were sweet and George loved them. He told them stories about Queenie and her pups. He told them about Rosie and how he hoped to find her sometime.

He sang them to sleep with the same song he had sung to Rosie. They begged for it every night—no other song would do.

After that George could study. His light burned always till midnight, and sometimes even later.

He hadn't written Jim to come yet. He wasn't settled—he'd wait awhile.

3. A Terrible Night

One night Mr. Simms forgot to lock his shop door, so he sent George to see to it.

"Just open the door and walk in," he said. "You'll find the key hanging over my desk."

George hurried to the shop. It was dark inside but he found the key, closed the door and tried to lock it. He had some trouble; the key didn't turn just right.

He stood on the step working with it. Suddenly a man seized him.

"Tryin' to break in, are you?" he yelled. "We've been watchin' you across the street."

Before George could speak the man called out, "Come on! I've got him!"

Men and boys came running from everywhere—from street corners, houses and stores.

"What was he up to, Bill?" asked a man.

"He was trying to break into the cooper shop. Caught him at it."

"No! No!" screamed the frightened boy. "I didn't—I wasn't—I——"

Bill Jones slapped him. "I saw you! Do you hear that? I saw you!"

"He's a thief!" cried a man.

"Take him to jail!" screamed a boy.

George tried to break away but he couldn't. Bill shook him roughly.

"Don't try that again. Hear what I said?"

George didn't answer. He was so frightened he couldn't speak.

Bill shook him again. "Answer me!" he shouted.

"Y-e-s-s——"

"Don't you say 'yes' to me! You have to say 'sir' and you know it."

"Y-e-s, sir," whispered George.

"Louder!" yelled Bill.

"Louder!" screamed the mob.

George couldn't speak at all now. His strength was gone—he thought he was dying.

Then a man pushed his way through the crowd and up to the shop.

"Here's the cooper!" cried a man. "I went after him."

"Let that boy alone!" cried Mr. Simms. "He lives in my home! I sent him here to lock the shop—I had forgotten."

Bill Jones freed George without a word. The crowd melted away and Mr. Simms and George started home.

George could hardly walk. The cooper had to help him. Then he undressed the poor frightened boy and put him to bed.

He brought him hot milk and sat by his bed till George went to sleep.

The next morning he went in to see how George was, but the bed was empty. George had gone!

IX

THE LITTLE WANDERER

1. From Town to Town

A LITTLE dark figure hurried out of Fort Scott at dawn with a small bundle. It was George Carver with his Sunday shirt. His books were all at school.

He hated to leave the Simms family like this, running away in the dark. But if he waited, the children would cry and coax him to stay. And he was afraid he would; he thought so much of them.

He wanted to get away from this town; he was afraid of Bill Jones. He wouldn't even wait to get his books.

He had made up his mind to leave during the night. He had awakened remembering something Mr. Simms had said on the way home.

"Bill will never hear the last of this. The men will tease him and laugh at him all over town. I shouldn't be surprised if he left."

Now George was just a young boy, but he was smart about things. He knew who would have to leave town—he, George Carver.

Bill Jones would drive him out, so the men would forget about him. He'd better go now and keep out of trouble.

When dawn came he was ready. He had folded his one good shirt and tied it in a bandanna handkerchief. He had nothing else to take.

Then he slipped out of the house quietly and took the road to the nearest town, Walton.

An hour later a good-natured farmer stopped his team and asked George to ride in his wagon.

"I reckon my mules can pull you and your bundle," he said with a smile. "Jump in!"

He told funny stories and jokes all the way.

A good-natured farmer stopped his team and asked George to ride
in his wagon.

114

George laughed so much he had almost forgotten Bill Jones when they reached Walton.

He found a barn to sleep in and hid his bundle in the hayloft. By noon he had found work, washing dishes in a restaurant.

"Yes, you can work before and after school," the manager said. "You can take off your coat, roll up your sleeves and begin right now. We're short of help."

"I'll have to find out about the school first, sir."

"What do you have to know? There's just one school in town."

"Oh!" said George. He was disappointed. He knew that would be for white children since there was only one.

"Then I can't stay here, Mr. Ross. I'll have to find a town where I can go to school. I'm past thirteen now and I want to finish the sixth grade this year."

"Well, what's to hinder you?"

"What's to hinder me?" asked George. Then he understood and a smile spread over his face. "Do you mean to say they'll let me enter?"

"Of course. Why not?"

"Why, I'm black."

"Pooh! We don't pay any attention to that here. We believe in everyone going to school, black, red, white and yellow."

George took off his coat, rolled up his sleeves and went to work. And the first thing he knew he heard himself singing.

"I want to keep that boy," the manager told the Negro cook. "I like to hear him sing over his work."

In two weeks George had bought his books; he was in school and getting along fine.

He didn't neglect his work, either. He knew how to wash dishes, thanks to Mrs. Carver and Mrs. Watkins.

"I don't see how he finds time to study," said the manager one day.

The cook smiled. "You don't know the half of it, Mr. Ross. That boy helps Negro children with their lessons right along. Seems like he can make things clear to them better than their teacher."

"I hope he gives them some of his own courage."

"He does, sir, he does. He helped my children and I saw the difference right away. They began to plan what they were going to do when they grew up."

"I suppose they all want to be like George?"

"Of course, and I wish they could, but there can't be anyone like him. He's different somehow."

"He is indeed, Bert."

2. *Bad Luck and Good Luck*

Just before Christmas George received a letter from his brother. Jim wrote he had quit school and was learning a trade—the plasterer's trade.

George was sorry that Jim didn't like to study. "I'll write him to come to Walton," he thought. "He can find work here and we can live together."

But before this letter was written the restaurant closed and George was out of work. Still worse, he couldn't find any.

He was down to ten cents when he heard there was work in a town not far away.

So early the next morning he was on his way there. He walked, he rode with farmers, he walked again and finally came to Newton.

He had good luck here from the first. He found work in the Grover Greenhouse.

Now he was happy. He was working with

plants. He was holding them in his hands again. He was watching them grow and bloom. He almost sang out loud in school.

If he could only stay here till he was ready for high school! That would be just one more year.

And maybe Jim would come. He'd write him this very Sunday.

Saturday something happened that put an end to writing that letter before it was even started.

Johnnie Grover accused George of taking his pocket knife. He hadn't seen George take it; he hadn't seen him use it. He had no reason to accuse him.

George said he didn't have the knife and Mr. Grover believed him.

"Johnny is always losing his things," he said. "He'll find his knife someday."

Sure enough he did find it, but the joy had gone from George's heart. He had been hurt, deeply hurt.

"He accused me because I'm black," he thought.

Jim had told him such things might happen. "You've got to get used to it, George," Jim had said. "You've got to smile and bear it."

But George couldn't smile; he couldn't bear it. He told Mr. Grover he was leaving that very day.

Work wasn't easy to find now, so from town to town he went; from barn to barn; from job to job and from school to school.

Sometimes he went hungry but he never begged. Even if he hadn't eaten for two days, he would not beg.

He hadn't written Jim for a long time now. He was never sure where he would be the next week or even the next day.

He wasn't sure of anything except that somehow, somewhere he was going to finish that sixth grade of school this year.

X

TUCKS, PLEATS AND RUFFLES

1. George Learns Fancy Ironing

"GET your iron in the corners, George," said Mrs. Lucy Seymour. "You missed that little tuck under the sleeve."

"I'll get it, Aunt Lucy."

"You never ironed this kind of a dress before, did you?"

"No, ma'am. But I'm good on shirts."

"I know you are. That's why I took you in. I tried you out on a shirt, a fine-pleated one, too. Couldn't have ironed it better myself."

"Why, thanks, Aunt Lucy, thanks."

"How did you happen to come here—to colored folks? Why didn't you go to rich white folks for work?"

"I heard you were the best ironer in town. I thought you might need help."

Aunt Lucy smiled. She knew folks said that and she was proud of it.

"Besides, I like to iron," George went on.

"Get your iron in the corners, George. You missed that little tuck under the sleeve."

"Here's something that's nothing but a lot of wrinkles. You use your iron and in two shakes here it is, all shining and beautiful."

"That's the way I feel about it, George. We'll get along fine. Chris likes you, too. He said it was like our own son was with us. He died when he was twelve."

"I'm glad you took me in, Aunt Lucy. It's nice to live in a real house again."

"You've had too many barns in your life, child. How old did you say you were?"

"Fourteen and a half."

"And you're in the eighth grade?"

"Yes, ma'am."

"And you didn't start to school till you were ten?"

"No, ma'am."

"That makes eight grades in four years."

"Yes, ma'am."

"You've made your own living all the time,

too. You've never had anyone to give you anything."

"No ma'am. Jim would help me if he could
but he can hardly make enough to live on."

Aunt Lucy wiped tears from her eyes.
"George," she said softly, "the colored folks
ought to be mighty proud of you. I know I am.
Chris is, too."

"I wish my father and mother knew how I'm
doing in school."

"Maybe they do." Then Lucy Seymour broke
down and cried. "You poor child," she sobbed.
"You poor, poor child."

"But I'm getting along, Aunt Lucy. I'm getting along all right."

"Here, iron that ruffle again, George. There's
a little crease in it."

"I'll get it out."

"I have to be careful; I get five dollars for this
dress."

"Five dollars!"

Mrs. Seymour nodded. "It takes 'most all day to iron it. Just look at the pleats and tucks and ruffles. It has to stand up alone when it's finished, too."

"Isn't it too thin?"

"I've been worrying about that. Can't put any more starch in it. Thin goods look bad too stiff."

"Well!" exclaimed George after a while. "I'm through."

"Hold it up by the top. Now then, stand it."

George obeyed, but the dress fell to the floor.

"He, he, he!" cackled someone at the door. It was Granny, the old Negro herbwoman who lived near.

"He, he, he!" she cackled again as she came into the room. "Let me see that dress."

George had picked it up and laid it on the ironing board. Granny felt the goods carefully.

"Mrs. Bell is going to be awful mad," said

Lucy. "She wants it for a party tonight but she won't wear it 'less it stands."

"Can't stand," declared the old woman. "Too thin."

"She won't pay me for my work."

"I'll just fix her—I'll put a spell on her."

"Hush that talk, Granny. I don't believe in putting spells on folks."

Granny paid no attention. She went right on talking.

"Can't abide that old Mrs. Bell. She wouldn't buy my medicine this morning. Walked away out to her big house on the river."

"Lots of folks don't believe in herb medicine."

"Well," Granny declared stubbornly, "she's not goin' to no party. She's not goin' to wear that dress tonight. Listen!"

Granny closed her eyes, rocked her body from side to side, waved her hands slowly and spoke softly.

"Shiver and shiver, lady mine,
    You don't wear that dress so fine.
    Lay your cheek on the pillow low,
    To that party you don't go.
    Burn and burn in your head
    Till you pay the price you said."

Then Granny left, as suddenly as she had come.

George was astonished. "Can she really do that?" he asked.

"No, of course not. She just pretends to put spells on folks. She thinks she'll sell more medicine, I reckon."

George smiled and turned to the ironing board. "What will you do about the dress?"

"You're going to take it to Mrs. Bell right now. Tell her it's the best I can do."

"What if she won't pay for the work?"

"I can't do a thing; it's a day's work lost."

"You burned your coal all day to heat the irons, too."

"It adds up, George. It adds up to a heap of money."

"It isn't right for you to lose it!" said George indignantly.

"A lot of things aren't right in this world, my boy. And if you don' know that now, you'll sure learn it."

2. The Magic Spell

George took the dress to the fine big house on the river. He had started to the kitchen door when the front door opened and a young lady called to him.

"Come in this way!"

George followed her into the hall and then into a sitting room on the right. There on a sofa sat the rich Mrs. Bell. She was wrapped in a large woolen shawl and a blanket was over her knees.

"I feel the draft from that front door, Mary," she said. "I'm shivering."

"Shivering," thought George. "Granny said she'd shiver."

"The door's closed now, Mother." Then pretty Miss Mary turned to George. "Well," she said with a smile, "let's see the dress."

George handed the bundle to her. The dress was wrapped in a nice clean towel and it was folded carefully.

Mary shook it out and smiled. "Oh, it's beau-

Mary smiled. "Oh! It's beautiful!" she cried. "Did you do it?"

tiful!" she cried. "I've never seen such ironing. Did you do it?"

"Yes, ma'am."

"See if it can stand alone," ordered her mother. Mary tried but the dress fell.

"Take it back, boy!" cried Mrs. Bell. "Take it back! I won't have it! I won't pay for it!"

"But, Mother, I wouldn't wear it if she made it stiff."

"Oh!" cried George. "Is it your dress? Are you going to the party?"

"Yes, indeed, it's mine," Mary answered. "And yes, indeed, I'm going to the party. I'm going to wear this dress, too."

Suddenly Mrs. Bell threw off her shawl and pushed the blankets aside. "Mary!" she cried. "I'm burning up. It's my fever again."

"Lie down, Mother. Put your head on this pillow. I'll call the doctor."

"Head—pillow—burn—burn——" thought George. "That's what Granny said."

Out in the hall, Mary gave him five dollars and said she wanted him to iron all her dresses.

George told his story as soon as he got home. Lucy was flabbergasted.

"Do you reckon Granny did put a spell on her, Chris?"

"No," answered Chris. "Granny saw she had a bad cold this morning. She knew it was fever and chills: Granny is a pretty good doctor herself."

"She put her spell on the wrong lady," said George. "It was Miss Mary's dress. She was the one who was going to the party."

"Ha, ha!" laughed Lucy.

"Ha, ha," laughed Chris and George.

XI

ARTIST GEORGE CARVER

1. Jimpson-Weed Flowers

THE next time George took his laundry to the kitchen door; Miss Mary wasn't about. The colored cook said she was in her studio and she wanted George to bring the dress there. Then she led him to a little room back of the parlor. And there was Miss Mary painting at an easel.

She looked at the dress and said it was wonderful the way George had ironed it. She gave him five dollars and didn't even test it.

"Aren't you going to see if it will stand up?" George asked.

"Will it?"

"Yes. It's heavier goods than the other dress."

"I'll take your word for it. Now then, I'll show you the picture I'm working on."

She led George to the easel. There on the canvas was painted a bowl of lovely white flowers.

"Oh!" cried the boy. "Jimpson-weed blooms!"

"I call them angel trumpets," said Mary smiling.

George didn't smile. To Mary's surprise he frowned. "Don't you like them?" she asked.

"They don't droop like that; they stand up more. Look—I'll show you."

He took a pencil from a table and a sheet of drawing paper. Quickly he drew a jimpson-weed flower in a bowl.

"Why, it's better than mine!" cried Mary. "It's much better. You wonderful boy! Have you ever had drawing lessons?"

"No, but I know how they ought to look. I've been drawing flowers ever since I can remember."

"I wish I might see your drawings. Couldn't you bring some of them to me?"

"They're not on paper. I scratched them on bark with a sharp stone." Then he told her about his secret garden at Diamond Grove.

"You should be drawing flowers all the time, George. Why don't you?"

"Well, I don't have much time any more. You

"They don't droop like that," George said. "They stand up more."

see, I'm working my way through school. I'm in the eighth grade."

He could have said that he didn't have a cent to buy paper and pencils for drawing, but he didn't. He wasn't begging anyone for anything.

"Oh, please draw some flowers for me, George. It will help me with my work. Here, take this package of paper. And here are some splendid pencils. They're made especially for drawing."

George thanked her. He was so grateful Mary almost cried. In fact she did cry after he was gone.

"He's an artist," she thought. "He's a real artist, and he hasn't a chance. He's too poor to go to art school and there's no one to help him. If I had any money I'd help him myself."

Then she cried again because she knew her mother would never give her a cent to send a Negro boy to school.

2. *All Kinds of Flowers*

After this, George was always drawing flowers. That is, when he didn't have to wash or scrub or iron or cook or do some other hundred and one jobs.

George was always drawing flowers.

He was in school, too, and studied his lessons at night. How he ever found time to draw was a mystery but he did.

He drew the sunflowers growing in the back yard. He drew the hollyhocks in a vacant lot. He drew the zinnias blooming in Aunt Lucy's flower bed. He drew her four-o'clocks and bachelor's buttons and daffodils.

One day he saw a large rose bed in the flower garden of a beautiful home. He peeped through the fence and wished he could get inside. He wanted to be closer to these lovely tea roses. He wanted to study them and draw them.

The Negro gardener saw the boy and told him he could come inside and look at the flowers.

"Be careful of that pond," he said. "It's deep. I don't want you to fall in."

"I'll be careful, sir. I don't know how to swim."

Then the gardener went off to another part of the garden.

The bed of roses was just back of the pond. George had to walk around it to get to them.

"Oh!" he cried when he stood in front of them.

Their beauty almost took his breath away. He loved them so much tears came in his eyes.

He talked to them softly. "You're beautiful. You're the most beautiful things God ever made."

He touched a satinlike petal with one finger. He touched it gently, delicately. He breathed in their lovely odor.

Then he sat on the ground, took his drawing board and paper from under his coat and began to draw.

He was so wrapped up in this he didn't hear talking close by. The first thing he knew four big white boys were standing over him.

"Say," said one, "this is my yard. What are you doing here?"

George sprang to his feet. "The gardener let me come in," he said. "I wanted to draw these roses."

"Roses! Do you hear that?" he said to the other boys. "He wants to draw roses!"

The others screamed with laughter.

"Tear up his papers!" shouted one.

"Throw them away!" shouted another.

"Throw his board into the pond!" yelled the third boy.

"Let's throw him in, too!" yelled the fourth.

In an instant it all happened. They grabbed George's drawings and tore them up. They seized his drawing board and threw it into the pond. They seized George and threw him in. Then they ran away laughing.

George screamed. Then he went down, down—— The next thing he knew the gardener was rolling him on the grass.

"I sure am glad to see you open your eyes," he said. "I thought there for a minute or so you wouldn't."

"I—I——" began George feebly.

"Don't try to talk. Just lie still. They won't come back. They know what I'd do to 'em. And," he went on angrily, "I'm going to tell their fathers. They'll get a good licking, every last one of them."

That night George told the Seymours what had happened.

"I'd like to lick them myself!" exclaimed Chris indignantly.

"So would I," said Lucy, "but you'll never see those boys again. That is, you won't if you'll do what we want you to. Tell him, Chris."

"My work has been changed, George, and we're going to move to another town. We have to leave tomorrow."

"We want you to go with us," added Lucy. "We'll feel awful bad if you don't."

"Of course I'll go with you," said George. "You're my folks—you're the only folks I have, 'cept Jim. And he's wandering about looking for work."

So it was settled, and George moved with his good friends, Uncle Chris and Aunt Lucy.

XII

COULD IT BE ROSIE?

1. At the Blacksmith Shop

"How do you think you can help me?" asked Mike Murphy, the blacksmith. "You don't look strong enough to lift my hammer, let alone strike the anvil."

"I could clean the shop and bring in the coal and keep your fire going."

"I do all that myself. I live in that room there just back of the shop."

"Alone?"

"Yes, bub, I'm alone."

"I can cook for you and wash your clothes and mend them."

"Can you bake biscuits?"

"Yes, sir. I can make 'em so light they'll melt in your mouth."

"What's your name?"

"George Carver."

"Where have you been living?"

"In town with Mr. and Mrs. Seymour. I helped her wash and iron for my board. And I did odd jobs, too, for other people."

"What made you leave them? Didn't they treat you right?"

"They treated me fine but you see it's vacation and I've got to make some money for my clothes and schoolbooks."

"Couldn't you find any work in town?"

"I didn't look. I wanted to be in the country. I wanted to see farms and trees and cattle."

"How soon could you come here?"

"Right now."

"Good. It's right now I'll be needing you. The county fair opens next week. They'll be bringing the race horses through and I'll be busy all day long. I won't have time to cook for myself.

Besides, I love biscuits better than anything."

George moved in with his one small bundle. He slept in the loft on a pile of straw but it was clean straw. The quilt over it was clean, too, for George had washed it that morning.

He washed Mike's quilts and cotton work clothes. He ironed them and patched them. Mike was pleased. It had been a long time since anyone had taken care of him.

He was pleased with George's cooking, too. He said he had never eaten such biscuits and pies.

George helped him in the shop and kept it clean. Mike began to wonder how he ever got along without him.

Mike was a good-natured man. He always came to his meals smiling and with a joke to tell. This evening, however, he was as sour as a man could look.

"Had a couple of rascals today," he said.

"Mean ones, they were. Their own horses were scared to death of them. And that's one thing I can't stand—to see a man's horse afraid of him."

"Did they ride good horses?"

Rosie!

"The best—racers, both of 'em. One was a beauty. She was coal-black and had a white star on her forehead."

George jumped to his feet. "Rosie!" he cried. "It must be Rosie!"

Then he told Mike about his pet and how she was stolen.

"I wouldn't be surprised if it was your horse. I thought they had stolen them. They said they were going to race them somewhere."

"Did they say where?" asked George anxiously.

"No, but it might be at the fair next week. If it is they won't be riding these horses. They'll send them ahead, maybe by some other road."

"Couldn't I go to the sheriff and tell him?"

"Yes, you could. But how can you prove Rosie belongs to you?"

"Why, she'll know me—she'll act like it."

"Maybe she won't. It's been four years since they took her, hasn't it?"

"Yes . . ."

"Well, I don't know. Maybe she will and maybe she won't. But if those men come again I'll give you a sign. I'll strike my anvil like this——"

He struck the anvil with his hammer three times—three short strikes close together.

George nodded. "I'll understand," he said.

Mike continued: "I won't look at you and you mustn't look at me. Horse thieves are mighty suspicious. They're always afraid someone will know them and tell the sheriff."

"I won't look at you."

"And don't say a word about Missouri. They'd be suspicious about that, too."

"Yes, sir."

"Remember now—three short strikes close together."

"Yes, sir."

2. Three Short Strikes

Now there was a stream of horses, owners, trainers, jockeys, grooms and stableboys. All were on their way to the fair. A good many stopped at Mike's.

Day after day George watched and listened but the signal wasn't given. He was discouraged. Maybe they wouldn't race the horses at this fair. Maybe they'd never come here again!

Then one day he heard it—three short strikes on the anvil!

There were two rough-looking men in the shop at the time. They rode horses George had never seen. One glance was enough to prove that. Then he looked at the men closely—too closely. One of them noticed it.

"What are you lookin' at me for, bub?" he asked sharply. "Are you afraid you won't see me again?"

"Excuse me—I didn't think what I was doing."

"Maybe you thought you knew me," the man went on.

"No, sir—I haven't been here long."

"Where you from?" asked the other man.

He looked at the men closely—too closely. One of them noticed it.

"Where?"

"Yes, where. You'd better not lie to me, either."

"Missouri," said George. He thought he had to tell them.

"Where from in Missouri?"

"Diamond Grove."

The two men looked at each other. Then the first one said sharply, "Who did you live with?"

"Moses Carver."

"You ain't got no business here in Kansas," said the second man. "We don't want you Missouri Negroes up here. You're going back and you're startin' tonight."

"Yes, sir."

"If he's here tomorrow, we'll burn your shop down," said the first man to Mike.

"He'll go," said Mike. "Your horses are ready now."

The men rode away and they rode north. They took the road to the fair.

"I'm sorry, George, but you'll have to go. I told you they were mean ones, didn't I?"

"Yes, sir, you did."

"I feel mighty bad turning you out. Don't know how I can get along without you. We've been good friends, George."

"You needn't feel bad, Mike. I would be going anyway. I'm going to follow them till I find Rosie."

"That's a dangerous business, boy."

"I know it, but I'm going."

The next morning at dawn, George left his good friend, Mike Murphy. He didn't take the road south to Missouri. Instead, he went north, to the fair.

3. At the Race Track

By noon George had a job in the fair grounds cleaning stables. He had seen all the horses, but

Rosie wasn't among them. Maybe they'd bring her later on.

Two days passed. George slept in a haystack just outside the grounds. "It will be a good place to hide," he thought, "if those men come. I can slip through a crack in the fence so quickly they won't even see me."

The third day came. Still no Rosie. But there was a new horse in a stable all alone. She was so mean she had to be alone. Only her trainer could go near her and he carried a whip.

"I can't count on that horse racing," he said. "Her owners better be showing up."

That afternoon they came—those very men! George hid close by and waited for them to come out of the stable.

Pretty soon they came and George heard every word they said.

"She's got to race!" said one man angrily. "She was the fastest two-year-old in Missouri."

"Everyone there knew it, too," said the second man. "They all watched for the coal-black filly with the white star on her forehead."

George's heart almost stopped beating. It was Rosie!

"What's the matter with her?" asked the first man. "She's four now; she ought to run even better."

"She might miss something she was used to," said the trainer. "That makes 'em mean sometimes. I've seen horses refuse to eat because they were used to having some pet around."

Another trainer nodded his head. "I saw a horse get mean because they took her straw sun-hat away from her. They couldn't do a thing with her. Finally they put it on her head again and she was sweet as pie."

The other trainers laughed. The owners only scowled.

"Did your horse have any pet?" asked the first trainer.

"No-o. I can't remember any," answered one man.

"Maybe she was used to having some child around."

"Can't remember anyone special. Can you, Jake?"

"No, I can't. I don't believe in that stuff. It's nonsense. That mare has to run. Give her the whip. Use your spurs."

"I'm afraid of that, sir. She'd only rear and jump."

Then the men passed on and George heard no more.

He looked about. There was no one in sight, so he went to the stable. He was opening the door when a hand seized his arm and pulled him back. It was Uncle Joe, a Negro stable hand.

"Keep out dis stable, boy! Dat hoss will stamp on you an' kill you."

"I just want to look at her, Uncle Joe."

"Don' you go inside dat door! Dem's my o'dahs. You jes' take dis broom an' sweep the yahd al 'round dis stable."

George began to sweep. How could he get inside? Uncle Joe would be watching him like a hawk.

Then he had an idea. He'd try singing. He'd sing the same song—the one he sang at Diamond Grove. So he went around the stable sweeping and singing and listening.

Presently came a whinny from the horse. George sang again and stopped. Then the mare whinnied again.

The trainer had come back and was listening. Now George was singing again. Again the mare whinnied.

"What's this?" asked the trainer. "I never heard her whinny before."

"It's Rosie!" cried George.

He told the trainer everything and the man then took him into the stable.

"Rosie!" In another minute he was in the stall hugging the mare's handsome head. And Rosie was nosing in his pockets and whinnying and nickering.

"That settles it, George," said the trainer. "She's your horse. I thought there was something wrong. I'll see the sheriff about this."

The next day the sheriff arrested the two thieves and took them to jail.

Rosie was sent back to Diamond Grove to Mr. Moses Carver.

XIII
DISCOVERIES

1. George Explores the Country

GEORGE was fifteen. His health was better; his muscles were hard and he was wiry and strong. But Kansas hadn't helped him to grow much.

Just now he was too busy and too happy to worry about it. He was in the first year of high school. He was in a new town and he had work he loved in a greenhouse.

He was working with plants again. He was watching them sprout and grow and bloom. Sometimes he was drawing them. He wished he could paint them. But how could he ever buy paints?

He slept in the toolhouse, but he didn't mind

that. He went to sleep breathing the lovely odors of fresh earth and growing things.

Mr. Morton's greenhouse was a mile from the city and not far from the woods. This gave George the chance he was always looking for. Every morning he was up at dawn and by daylight he was in the woods.

He wasn't looking for anything special; he was just looking. He looked at plants and rocks. He looked at leaves and the bark of trees. He looked at the ground itself and wondered.

Here in the woods was black soil. The field over there was red clay, bright red. Another field was dark red clay. That hillside was blue clay. Down in the hollow was yellow clay.

"What lovely colors!" he thought. "They'd be wonderful for painting flowers." If he could only lift them out of the clay! But he couldn't; they were a part of it.

He wandered about, just looking. He learned

the country for miles around—the creeks and hills and hollows.

He went the long way to school, along the creek, instead of taking the road. He liked to look down through the clear water and see the rocks and pebbles on the bed.

One day he noticed a difference in the water—not all along, just in one spot near the city.

There was a thin scum on the creek here. It was blue with streaks of red and purple and it shone brightly in the sunlight.

He wondered about it. What made this scum? Did it come from certain plants? Had rain washed it down from the hills? Or did it come out of the ground?

He must find out. He'd come back when he had more time. He was due at the greenhouse in a little while.

Then he forgot it, he was so busy with his flowers and books.

2. Shanty Town

Close to the city and on both sides of the creek was a little village of huts. It was called Shanty Town and only Negro families lived there. There wasn't a single white person.

The land was low. Pools of water stood on it most of the time. It was a poor place for people and even worse for vegetables.

If plants could grow in the clay soil they were likely to rot in the standing water.

But there was one good thing about this place; there was a colored school here—a grade school and a high school in the same building.

George went to this high school and was making splendid grades. He had a good time here, too. He liked fun as well as anyone.

He belonged to the Boys' Club. He was one of the best singers in the Music Club. He took part in the plays of the Dramatics Club.

Before long he knew every family in Shanty

Town, for the boys were always taking him home with them.

If George didn't know how much Negro parents wanted their children to go to school, he found it out now.

They talked with him because they knew how he was struggling to learn. They told him they'd work their fingers to the bone to give their children an education.

They said they were glad they could live near a school even if the place wasn't fit to live in.

So one Monday afternoon George was surprised to see some of the families moving. He was on his way home and he couldn't stop to ask questions.

The next morning he saw others moving from other streets, a good many others. Wagons were piled high with furniture. Even wheelbarrows were being used.

Then George stopped. He had to find out about this even if he was late to school.

He asked several men about it but they were all too busy to talk. Finally he had to go on.

School wasn't the same this morning. The teachers were different somehow and the pupils were upset. George was upset himself. He knew something was going on that worried everyone.

At recess he found out—the boys told him.

"It's on account of that ghost," John explained. "It was walking through Shanty Town last night. I saw it myself."

"So did I," said Clyde. "I heard it groan, too."

"So did I! So did I!" cried the others.

"Oh, it was just someone playing a trick," declared George. "There's no such thing as a ghost."

"Of course not," John agreed. "Besides, I saw his big black shoes under his sheet."

"I saw them, too!" exclaimed Fred.

"So did I! So did I!" exclaimed the others.

"Then I don't see why the folks are moving out," said George.

"They think it's a warning," said John.

"A warning for us to get out," added Fred. "That's the way they do in Kansas when they want to get rid of us colored folks."

"My father thinks some white men want this land along the creek," said Clyde.

"My father thinks that, too," nodded John.

Then recess was over and the boys went to their rooms.

3. George Tries to Find Out

At noon George talked with the school janitor. "Why would white men want this land, Mr. Bird? There's a flood every time the creek is high and everyone has to move out till the water goes down."

"I can't understand it. Maybe it isn't the land

they're after. Maybe it's something else. But we've got to go whatever it is."

"Why don't you refuse to go?"

"We don't dare. They'd burn our houses right over our heads."

"They wouldn't do that, would they?"

"A bunch of rascals will do anything and that's what they are—rascals. The best class of white people have nothing to do with this. They don't like it. They told the teachers they don't."

Then the janitor went about his work and George went to his class.

That afternoon the teachers told the children to take their books home. They said the school would be closed.

Mr. Morton was indignant. "Those colored people belong here," he said. "They pay their taxes and obey the law. They are good citizens."

"If this was Diamond Grove I'd know what the white men were after," declared George.

"What?"

"Lead. There was lead on our farm and some men tried their best to get it. But Mr. Carver wouldn't sell it."

"It isn't lead here. It can't be any mineral: this country is too flat."

"Then what do they want, Mr. Morton?"

"Maybe they think the Negroes are getting too much work."

"They didn't try to scare the Negroes in the west part of the city. My teacher told me that— she lives over there."

"Well, there's some reason. I'll find out if I can. I'll go to the city tomorrow."

But it was George who found out first. That night he decided to investigate. By daylight he was on his way to the creek. He followed it for a mile or so until he came to the shanties. He had seen nothing so far.

Now the sun shone out bright and strong.

Suddenly he saw a gleaming brightness on the water. Why, it was that scum he had noticed before! It spread from shore to shore, blue with red and purple lights.

He dipped his fingers in it. Then he smelled them and his eyes nearly popped out of his head. It was oil he smelled!

He ran all the way to the greenhouse. "Mr. Morton!" he cried. "I know what the men want! It's on the creek!"

"What's on the creek? What have you found?"

"Coal oil! It's floating on the water! Smell my fingers, sir."

Mr. Morton sniffed at George's fingers. "Oh, that's just some coal oil the Negroes threw away. They didn't want to take it with them, I suppose."

"Is that it?" George was disappointed.

He dipped his fingers in the scum. Then he smelled them. It was oil!

"It couldn't be anything else. I never heard of coal oil being found on water."

Soon after this George left the city. He had to find a high school somewhere. He couldn't give that up.

He found a farmer driving to the next town and rode with him. An hour or so had passed when he suddenly remembered something. He had forgotten to tell Mr. Morton that he had seen that oily scum before.

Yes indeed, *before* the Negroes left Shanty Town! *Before* they emptied their oil cans, *if they did.*

XIV

THE GRADUATING CLASS

1. The Last Month

IT WAS George's last month in high school. He
was to graduate in June and he was the only
Negro in his class. The others were white boys.

George had worked his way through high
school. There was no one to buy clothes and
books for him. There was no one to see that he
had a place to sleep and food to eat. He had done
it all by himself.

It was hard for him to save money. He made
barely enough to live on from day to day. But he
had done it somehow.

No, it wasn't "somehow." He knew well
enough how he had saved pennies. It was by going without food. It was by wearing old clothes

and old shoes. He had suffered for every cent of his savings.

Now he had almost enough to buy his clothes for graduation. Just last Saturday he had gone to the stores to look for a suit, hat, tie and shoes.

Of course some of the schoolboys had seen him. Monday everyone in school knew. Everyone was glad, too, for they all liked George.

They even talked about his new clothes at home. Parents all over town knew that George's suit was gray and very neat. They heard about his new gray hat, blue tie and black shoes.

Oh no, he hadn't bought them yet, but he had selected everything, and now he had almost enough money.

Some of George's classmates offered to go with him when he was ready to buy. They said he wouldn't have to pay so much because they knew the merchants.

George's heart was filled with love for these

boys and for all the schoolboys. He was so happy he thought he'd never be any happier.

Then something sad happened. George didn't know it yet, but he would, soon.

Two white boys, Tom and Paul, had refused to sit on the platform on graduation day. They said they wouldn't even go up for their diplomas if that Negro sat on the stage.

The other boys in the class tried to get them to change their minds.

"Look how smart George is," said Ted.

"The color of his skin certainly didn't hurt his brain," declared Ray.

"What's color anyway?" asked Bob. "It's only skin-deep."

"Sure! That's right!" cried the others—all except Paul and Tom. They just sat there; they wouldn't say anything.

"Look how hard he's worked to get an education," Frank suggested.

"There was no one to help him, either," added Charlie. "And look how our folks have helped us!"

Again other boys cried, "Sure! That's right!"

But again Paul and Tom wouldn't say anything.

"George has nice manners, too," continued Jimmie. "He's always polite to everyone."

"I can't see why you boys don't want to sit by him," said Joe. "You've been sitting in the same classroom for two years."

"But this is different: it's graduation day," said Paul.

"Oh! You're afraid the visitors will see you!" exclaimed John.

Then Tom and Paul left the room. They were angry and they showed it plainly.

"They won't change," said Jimmie. "They've been listening to their grandmothers' talk. Those old ladies still think just what their grandmothers thought. My mother said so."

Charlie nodded. "Some folks used to think Negroes shouldn't even learn to read."

"That's a fact," agreed Ray. "They thought they wouldn't work if they were educated."

The others nodded. They had all heard this.

"George is going to feel awfully bad about it," said Bob.

"Maybe he won't have to know," suggested John. "Maybe the principal can persuade them to sit on the platform."

But the principal couldn't persuade them and he finally had to tell George.

The boy was broken-hearted. He had looked forward to this day for years. He had gone hungry for this day. He had worn ragged clothes. He had been lonely.

Now he was to be pushed off just because he wasn't the same color as the other boys. He felt he could not stand it. He wanted to run away and hide like some poor wounded animal.

Then he heard the principal talking. "I'm just as sorry as you are, George. I wouldn't have had this happen for anything. I don't want you to be hurt—you're too fine a boy."

"I—I don't know what to do, sir," George's voice was trembling.

"I want you on that platform," said the principal firmly. "You've earned your place there."

"I don't want to make trouble, sir."

"Well, we'll see. Perhaps it can be settled. I'll do my best."

That night George asked the Lord to tell him what to do.

2. How It Was Settled

The next morning the matter was settled but not by the principal or George or the two boys. It was Jim who settled it.

A letter came from him. He was sick and needed money. Could George lend him some? He would pay him back as soon as he could work again. He was among strangers, down in Arkansas. He'd been working there.

George didn't have to think this over. He sent all his money to Jim, every cent. And he was glad to do so.

Then he told the principal he couldn't sit on the platform graduation day. He said he couldn't get new clothes and he told the reason.

This news went through the school. It made everyone feel bad: *everyone,* for, strange to say, it did something to Paul and Tom. It touched their hearts more than anything their classmates had said.

Never before in all their lives had these boys realized that a Negro had such deep love for a brother.

"I didn't know they loved each other so much," said Tom.

"He sent all his money," said Paul. "He didn't keep back a cent for his clothes."

They were silent for a moment. Then **Paul** burst out: "I'll sit by him!"

"So will I!" cried Tom.

The principal was delighted to hear the good news and George's heart was again filled with happiness.

He planned to sit in the back row so he could hide his faded trousers and old shoes. No one would notice him much anyway. They were coming to see the other boys graduate. There wouldn't be anyone coming to see him.

"If my folks could come," he thought, "I'd have as many as any of them. There's Jim and the Carvers. There's Uncle Andy and Aunt Mariah and Uncle Chris and Aunt Lucy.

"And there's Miss Mary and Mike Murphy

and Mr. Morton. They'd all come if they could."

Well, it was a good thing they couldn't. He wouldn't want them to see him in his old clothes —not on graduation day.

3. The Class Play

The night before graduation the class gave a play. They had been rehearsing it for a month.

George was to take the part of a colored girl, a singer. He was given the part because he was so small and because he could sing. He had a high thin voice and could sing like a girl. He could act like a girl, too.

At rehearsals the others laughed at George until their faces ached. He mimicked the way girls walked. He mimicked the way they held their parasols. He danced and pranced and rolled his eyes. He was the funniest girl anyone had ever seen.

He wore a red dress all ruffles and pleats. His

hat was covered with flowers. He wore white lace mitts and carried a bright red parasol and a fan.

There was a villain in the play, of course. He stole the girl from her home up in the hills. Then he made her sing for him and his bad friends. She didn't want to do this so she watched for a chance to escape. She wore her hat all the time to be ready.

One day the villian turned his back. This was her chance! She grabbed her mitts and parasol and fan. Then away she went!

Next she sang in an army camp. But here came the villain lickety-split! She just had time to grab her mitts, parasol and fan. Then away she went again!

Now she was singing on a wharf to a boatload of sailors. But, alas, here came the villain in a little skiff. He was rowing like mad and he was talking to himself out loud.

"I aim to git the gal this time!" he shouted. "I aim to throw her into this here skiff, too! And I dare anybody to stop me! I dare 'em!"

Then an old Negro man jumped up from his seat in the front row.

"Watch out, Missy!" he cried. "He's a-comin'! I'll fix him."

He held up a rifle and aimed it at the villain.

"Hold on, Pappy!" yelled the girl. "Don't shoot him! I'm not a girl! Look, Pappy!"

George tore off his hat, dropped his dress to the floor and stepped out of it. There he was—a slender boy in blue jeans.

A man took the gun from the Negro and the audience roared with laughter. Then the curtain went down. The play had been a grand success.

Some folks thought the class had hired the old Negro. Some thought they hadn't. But all of them said George was the hit of the play. They said he was a born actor and he ought to go on the stage.

Back of the curtain the surprised young actor was opening a large box he had just received from Tom and Paul.

In this box was the gray suit George had selected, the tie, the hat and the black shoes.

There was a note in the box, too.

"DEAR GEORGE,

"Please accept this gift. We're ashamed of what we did.

"Your classmates
"PAUL
"TOM"

Tears came into George's eyes and a sob was in his throat.

"Dear Lord," he prayed that night, "I thank Thee for these presents. Now they won't be

ashamed of me on the platform. I thank Thee,
dear Lord."

4. Graduation Day

The ten graduates sat on the platform, nine
white boys and one Negro. They sat in a semi-
circle—George couldn't hide behind anyone.

He didn't want to hide now. He was proud of
his nice new clothes. He was proud to be here.

It made his struggles and hard work worth
while. He didn't regret any of it.

"Why," he thought, "I'm not even sorry I'm
black. I believe I'm proud of it. Yes, I am proud
of it. Everything was against me but I've won."

Now his name was called and he stood. The
diplomas had been given to them. Why was the
principal calling his name? He was puzzled.

The principal announced: "The prize for
the best grades in English for the year goes to
George Carver. Ten dollars."

Now his name was called. He stood up.

George bowed and sat down. But again his name was called and again he stood.

The principal announced: "The prize for the best grades in Science ever made in this school or any other high school in Kansas, goes to George Carver. Fifteen dollars."

George bowed again and sat down. But a third time he had to stand.

The principal announced: "The prize for the best art work of the year goes to George Carver. Ten dollars."

The audience clapped their hands and cheered. The band played. The principal shook hands with George.

Then his classmates crowded about him and patted him on the back and told him they were proud of him.

They were proud of George. They were glad that splendid boy had won the prizes. They knew he deserved them.

That afternoon George took the train for Arkansas, thanks to the prize money. He was going to see Jim.

After that he would visit the Carvers and Rosie.

After that he would go to Neosho to see Uncle Andy and Aunt Mariah.

Then he would visit Uncle Chris and Aunt Lucy and Mike Murphy.

He'd call on Miss Mary and look at her paintings.

After that he didn't know. He might go to college. He'd have to work his way through but that didn't matter.

Hadn't he always worked his way through everything? Hadn't he always found friends along the way?

XV

PROFESSOR GEORGE CARVER

1. Waiting at the Union Station

THE railroad station in Washington, D. C., was crowded and not with travelers, either. The people were waiting to see a great man. He was coming on the next train from Alabama.

This man was one of the greatest scientists in the United States. He was a Negro and his name was Carver—George Washington Carver.

He had made so many wonderful discoveries in science, the whole world had heard of him. His name was in the newspapers almost every day. Of course people wanted to see him.

Some high-school pupils were waiting close to the gates to the train shed.

"I wouldn't miss seeing him for anything,"

said a boy. "He's the first man in the world to make things out of peanuts. Why, he made paper out of the shells!"

"He made three hundred things out of peanuts!" exclaimed another boy.

"He made one hundred and eighteen things out of sweet potatoes!" exclaimed another.

"I never heard anything like it!" a girl said.

"No one else ever did," declared a man who stood near. "Professor Carver is a wonderful man."

"Does he teach?" asked another girl.

"He teaches in Tuskegee Institute in Alabama. It's a college for Negroes and it's a very beautiful place."

"What does he teach?" asked a boy.

"Soils and plants. And I can tell you no man in the world knows more about them than Mr. Carver."

"Was he named after George Washington?" a girl asked.

"No, he wasn't. There's a little story about his middle name. Would you like to hear it?"

"Yes! Yes!" cried the girls and boys.

"When Mr. Carver was a young man in college he found that another George Carver was getting his mail. So he decided to give himself a middle name."

"Then he'd get his own letters," a boy said.

The gentleman nodded. Then he went on: "Mr. Carver thought of Henry and Sam and Louis and Fred, but he didn't quite like them.

"Then he thought of Frank and Robert and Ben and Charlie, but he didn't quite like them. He couldn't decide which name sounded best with George and Carver.

"One day he suddenly thought of Washington and that settled it. He became George Washington Carver at once. And that's the way it happened."

"Well! Well!" exclaimed the boys.

"Well! Well!" exclaimed the girls.

A group of college students were just behind the high-school pupils.

"He worked his way through Ames College in Iowa," said one. "He had a little laundry of his own and washed for the students."

"Yes," said another, "he cleaned up some shirts but he 'cleaned out' the whole college on prizes."

The others laughed and nodded. They had heard how George Carver took almost all the prizes when he graduated from Ames.

"Did you know he took a prize for painting?" asked one.

"Painting!" exclaimed the others. That was one prize they didn't know about.

"He painted beautiful flower pictures. They say you can't tell them from real flowers. And where do you think he got his paints? No, he didn't buy them."

The others shook their heads.

"From clay—red clay, blue clay, yellow clay. He discovered a way to get the colors from the soil."

The students whistled. They were too surprised to say anything.

Three army cooks were waiting also.

"I'm glad my regiment is close to Washington," said one. "I've been wanting to see Mr. Carver for a long time. He knows more about foods than any cook I ever heard of."

"He certainly does," agreed another. "Why, he made pies out of sour grass! I've heard they tasted fine."

"He made pies out of curled dock, too," said

the third cook. "I've heard they were as good as rhubarb pies."

"Yes, and he made flour out of sweet potatoes. Then he made bread out of the flour," said the second. "It was good, too, as good as wheat bread."

"He could get up a meal out of weeds," declared the first. "He said there were enough growing in fence corners to feed an army."

"Wonder what the soldiers would say if we gave 'em a stew made out of cockleburs," smiled one.

"Or soup made out of thistles," smiled the second.

"Or grass sandwiches," smiled the third.

"Ha, ha, ha!" laughed the army cooks.

A group of Negroes were also waiting to see one of the greatest men of their race.

"Professor Carver has a great many visitors,"

said a teacher from Tuskegee. "Men come from everywhere to see his laboratory in the college and to ask his advice."

"I suppose farmers come to ask why their crops fail," suggested a lawyer.

"Yes, sir, they do. Professor Carver helped a thousand or more last year. And here's an interesting thing, gentlemen. He helped as many white farmers as black."

"I should think he'd help the Negroes first," exclaimed a doctor. "He has said over and over that he wanted to help his own race."

"Surely the Negro farmers needed his help more," added a merchant.

"Dr. Carver pays no attention to color," explained the teacher. "If a man needs help he gives it freely. He wants the whole South to produce more food."

"Is that story about the pecan trees true?" asked a woman.

"It is indeed. Some kind of a blight struck the trees and hundreds died. Then Professor Carver found a cure and saved the rest."

"He saved the pecan-nut business, too, both South and North," declared a grocer.

"I understand a good many big scientists visit him," said a reporter.

"I should think they would," put in a brick mason. "Wouldn't they like to know how he made paving bricks from cotton!"

"And imitation marble from wood shavings," added a carpenter.

"And baskets from tomato vines!" exclaimed a woman.

"He seems able to make something out of everything," said a minister.

The teacher nodded. "He says nothing should be wasted."

"I hear he never charges for his advice," said

a bank clerk. "I can't understand that. He's not a rich man: he gets a small salary."

"He gives away half of that, I've heard," added a woman. "They say he's always helping the poor Negro girls and boys in the college."

"It's true," the teacher agreed. "He says he remembers what a struggle he had to get through school."

"He could help more of them if he charged for his advice and assistance," declared the bank clerk. "He'd have more money to give away."

"I've said that a hundred times," said the doctor.

"So have I," said the lawyer.

"I think I can explain it," the minister suggested. "He doesn't want to think of selling and buying and prices for this and that. It would take too much of his time. He needs it all for his discoveries."

"You are right," said the teacher. "That is his reason."

A policeman now cleared a path through the crowd for several gentlemen. They were finely dressed and wore high silk hats and white gloves.

They were all well-known teachers of science in Northern colleges. They were here to greet a famous teacher of science. It didn't matter to them that his skin was black. They were interested in his mind.

The policeman led them to the gates and the high-school boys had to move back.

"The train from Alabama is in," said the gateman.

The gentlemen watched the platform closely for a few minutes.

"There he is!" exclaimed Professor L——. "That Negro with the suitcase!"

"It couldn't be!" exclaimed Professor R——.

"He wouldn't be dressed like that. He's to go straight to Congress."

"He pays no attention to clothes," explained Professor L——. "I went to Tuskegee to see him last year. I know him."

"But Congress has invited him to speak!" cried Professor M——. "It's a great honor. Doesn't he know that?"

Professor L—— smiled. "His mind is so full of his discoveries he has no time to think of clothes."

The shabby colored man came through the gates. No porters rushed to carry his suitcase. It was large, too, and heavy.

The professors now surrounded him. They took off their silk hats. They shook hands with him. They said they were very glad to meet him and they meant it.

Now porters came running. Four tried to get Mr. Carver's suitcase.

The shabby colored man

came through the gates.

"No," he said politely. "I must carry this my-self."

Then he turned to the gentlemen. "It holds my peanut exhibit for Congress. It's as precious as diamonds."

2. Professor Carver Before Congress

A little later Professor George Washington Carver stood before the Congress of the United States in the Capitol. He was telling them about his work with peanuts. He had been speaking ten minutes.

He wasn't half through but his time was up so he sat down. His invitation had said he would be given ten minutes.

"Go on! Go on!" shouted the Congressmen. Then Professor Carver opened his suitcase and showed them samples of some of the products he had made from peanuts.

Milk	Sauces
Butter	Oils
Cheese	Shaving Lotions
Candies	Dyes
Coffee	Lard
Pickles	Linoleum
Flour	Breakfast Foods
Soap	Ink
Face Powder	Paper

"There are some two hundred and eighty-two other peanut products," he said. "Also I have discovered thirty-two kinds of milk in peanuts and each is richer than cow's milk."

The Congressmen were astonished. They asked many questions and kept Mr. Carver talking for more than an hour.

Then someone wanted to know what he had made out of sweet potatoes.

"I have made one hundred and eighteen products so far," he answered, "and I expect to make many more. Here are a few of them."

Flour	Laundry Bluing
Starch	Shoe Blacking
Paste	Yolk of egg
Dye	Ginger
Molasses	Ink
Vinegar	Rubber

Again the Congressmen were astonished. They thanked Professor Carver, and when he left they stood to show their respect for him.

"He's the most amazing man in the world," said one.

"He forgot to tell us about an oil he made from peanuts," said a Congressman D——. "I read about it in the papers."

"Speaking of oil," said Congressman S——, "reminds me of a story. Out in Kansas they've found coal oil in the very place Mr. Carver said they'd find it when he was a boy in school there. He discovered it floating on a creek."

"It's too bad it didn't make him rich," said one.

"He doesn't care about money," said another. "His one thought is to help others. That's the thing he lives for."

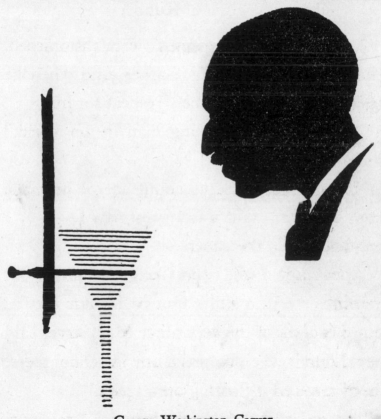

George Washington Carver.

The Congressmen nodded gravely. They knew they had been listening to a man with a great heart and a great soul—a man who would make any sacrifice to help mankind.

THE END